VAF

C000244862

To Gemma,

With love & solidarity,

Julie Jacques/'21

T

I

O

N

S

VARIA

JULIET JACQUES

Published by Influx Press
The Greenhouse
49 Green Lanes, London, N16 9BU
www.influxpress.com / @InfluxPress
All rights reserved.

Printed and bound in the UK by TJ Books.
Paperback ISBN: 9781910312773
Ebook ISBN: 9781910312780
Cover design: Austin Burke
Interior design: Vince Haig

CONTENTS

A NIGHT AT THE THEATRE

This diary, which provides an invaluable insight into early Victorian London's cross-dressing subculture, was recently passed to the Bishopsgate Institute's LGBT library by a descendent of 'Simon', one of the people involved. The donor declined to give Simon's surname, and we respect the family's wishes. We do know, however, that 'James Goldsand' was born in Surrey in 1821, but we have been unable to trace him beyond the mid-1840s – it is possible that he changed his name, or left the country, but his fate will most likely remain a mystery.

....

Tuesday, 17th March, 1846.

I found this article in the 'Police' section of The Times to-day:

> BOW-STREET. –Yesterday a young man, in woman's clothes, named John Travers, was placed at the bar before Mr. Hall, charged with frequenting the public streets for an unlawful purpose.
>
> This was the second or third case of the kind which has been brought under the notice of the Court within the past few weeks.

I bought a second copy, cut out the article and posted it to Simon, with a letter.

Dear Sir,

This article came to my attention. It details a crime of the most abominable nature, and a vice that is becoming increasingly prevalent in our city. It is imperative that you pay me a visit, so that we can discuss how to promote greater vigilance; I suggest meeting this Saturday.

Yours,

A Concerned Citizen.

Thursday, 19th March, 1846.

I received this reply to my letter to-day. Preventative measures *indeed!*

> *Sir,*
>
> *The report that you sent induced feelings of the greatest disgust in me, and you are right to be concerned. I agree that we must assist the authorities in preventative measures. I shall visit you on Saturday.*
>
> *Sincerely,*
>
> *A Dagger-bearer.*

Saturday, 21ˢᵗ March, 1846.

Simon came to my lodging-house at ten o'clock in the morning. I opened the door and saw him with a sly grin on his face, his brown eyes lit with mischief. I ushered him inside before I put my arms around him and kissed him on the cheek. He paused for a moment, and then brushed past, looking beyond me to the stains on the floor, and immediately declared my place to be 'as disgusting as Devil's Acre', asking how much 'those charlatans' were extorting me for it. When I told him it was three bob a week, he said that was 'the very definition of *dirt-cheap*'.

I agreed about the *dirt*, I told him, but said that my weekly spending on coals was ruining me. As my clothes shop has all the vibrancy and vitality of a pauper's funeral, I said that I had just one remaining option – getting married. I watched his face, wondering if his expression might sink at the thought of my being betrothed, but he just laughed. 'The confirmed bachelor!' he said. 'Seriously, my good fellow, you would have to find a lady who was born *yesterday*.'

I told him that I didn't know *what* he meant, suggesting

that I marry someone like Phoebe Hessel. When he asked who this was, I showed him a cutting from one of my old journals about how Hessel disguised herself as a man to join the Army.

'That's all well and good until your wife gets posted to Australia,' he replied. 'That said, if they find out about you, they'll transport you out there to accompany her.'

I asked him how 'they' would ever know. Imagine that you have joined the Metropolitan Police or trained to become a man of law, I asked. Would you waste *your* time on a married man when so much vice stalks the capital's streets?

Simon looked over at my suitcases and asked what might happen if the landlady opened them. She bloody well would, too, I said, knowing she'd been rooting around in Collins' place, which is why I keep them under lock and key. However, it still hasn't occurred to her to check under the bed. If she ever did, I said, I would tell her that I was in a play. And if she did not believe me, I was sure that I could find another lodging-house, just as luxurious.

I pulled out a case and opened it, telling Simon that the landlady was away, visiting her old dear in the countryside, and would not return until tomorrow. Then I showed him the blue frock that I'd ordered to the shop, saying I had told the dressmaker it was for one of our mannequins. As my mind fell back to those wonderful evenings after every customer had left, with the front door locked and the window blacked out, struggling to put on and take off the most troublesome items, I told him how this dress followed the fashion of to-day, with its narrow sleeves, low shoulders and a bell-shaped skirt, and only best crinoline. When he told me to be quiet because somebody might hear us, I said it was a present for my sister. Nobody *knew* that I didn't have a sister, after all, but some time, depending on what they saw, I might have to tell them that I did.

'Oh, no ...' said Simon, his eyes rolling and his jaw dropping. I showed him the *Times* article pointing out the passages about how Travers went to 'the public thoroughfares near the club-houses in Pall-mall East', and the streets around it. Simon pointed out that Travers got caught, 'because the police thought he was a dollymop'. But that was only because he kept going to the same place and someone blew on him. The Peelers had thought he was a woman, and just told him to move on. When Simon said that 'wasn't what happened to the men at Mother Clap's molly house', I simply said that we wouldn't go there – not difficult, since it was raided 120 years ago.

Simon took the newspaper and read aloud from the Travers report: 'Inspector Partridge said, that from what had come to his knowledge, he was satisfied that the object of the prisoner and his associates, in frequenting the parks and streets, was either to steal or to obtain money by practices of the most revolting or unnatural character.'

'Heavens, James,' declared Simon. 'He was lucky not to be hanged!'

I repeated Travers' defence that it was just a bet that he 'would pass undetected in his disguise' and 'a mere frolic.' Simon said the court didn't believe Travers, and asked if *I* would. Perhaps, I replied, if I'd only seen him once or twice. Simon looked at me, full of doubt. This brought back all the times in Goldsand's Dressmakers when Simon had come in: that first afternoon, when he said he wanted something for his wife's birthday and I soon identified a kindred spirit; the way he would sit on the window-ledge and make conversation, for an hour or more when the inspiration struck him; the times when he came after leaving his solicitors' office, once the shop has closed, and we pulled down the shutters, lit the candles and had dinner together, him in his suit and me as his wife …

I said that if I went to Pall-mall then perhaps I *would* get caught, at least if I went too often, or if I spoke to strange men. But once – just *once*, I repeated – wouldn't it be wonderful to walk the streets as Jennifer?

'*Will* it be once?' he asked. I said I didn't know, but that it would be awful to go to the grave without trying it. He enquired about whether that would be 'worse than gaol, or the gallows'. None of that would happen, I suggested, as long as nobody thought I was a margerie; I told him that we would keep away from the 'dark courts and narrow passages'.

As the word 'we' left my lips, Simon's eyes widened, and he turned his cheek to me. I asked him if he would keep guard; he replied that it was 'one thing keeping such matters behind closed doors', but that 'going out in public was quite another'. But once I was done up, I insisted, no-one would ever suspect me, and that we would be fine if we did not go to the wrong places.

'Where are the *right* places?' asked Simon.

I said they were the ones in the newspaper: Holborn, Fleet-street, and Leicester-square.

Simon said that 'the police will be onto those by now'. I suggested that we go to the theatre, as man and wife. Who would even look twice at us? Next time, I offered, we could go somewhere else, maybe even assuming the opposite roles.

'*I'm* not going out in all those petticoats,' he said. 'If you really *have* to do this, then I will pretend that you– we – are doing it for a bet, but if they fine you *100l* like they did Travers, then I cannot help.'

What's *100l* next to one night of being myself, I replied, telling him that next Friday, *Twelfth Night* was playing at the Drury-lane Theatre, costing one and sixpence for the lower gallery. Wouldn't that be fun? I asked.

'If ending up at Bow-street is your idea of fun, then yes,' said Simon. I said that if this came to pass, then the whole thing was my idea – a lark amongst friends. They would likely let us go. When he said it would be 'completely humiliating', I told him the next stage of the plan. We would tell the police that his name was Robert Hopkins and that he was a labourer. I would be George Watson, bricklayer. That way, nobody would ever know that we were there.

Simon said that 'nobody would ever believe' that I was a bricklayer – not with my 'pathetically weak forearms'. I thought that any court would be so shocked that they would believe anything, and that they would be far less concerned if they thought they weren't dealing with gentlemen. He just sighed. I asked if we had a deal.

'If you absolutely *must* ...'

Saturday, 28th March, 1846.
Wearing his finest black tie, Simon came at five o'clock in the afternoon to help me prepare. I got out my frock, petticoats, shoes, corset, bonnet and wig and laid them on the bed, blacking out the window so that no-one could see. My whole body was shaking with anticipation, although I was trying not to get *too* excited. I took some deep breaths

to calm myself. I undressed. I asked Simon if he might help me with my corset, just before that glorious moment where he pulled the cord tight. As he laced it up, he enquired if I *had* to wear it, as it looked awfully painful; I replied that the frock wouldn't have the right shape without it. Then I grasped the bedpost with both hands as he put it around my stomach, laced it up and pulled as hard as he could. I yelped. He hissed at me to be quiet, worried that people may hear. Then he looked at my chest, his expression more confused than anything else, and asked, 'What are you going to do about ...'

I pointed him towards two items I'd made out of left-over fabric and wool during my spare time at the shop, resting on my table. Smiling, I asked if he wanted to put them in. He sighed, held my shoulders so that I would be still, and placed them into the cups on my corset. I loved how gently he moved them, taking every care to get them in the right place. Then I put on my little white trousers with the frills around the ankles. He asked what I needed those for, given that nobody would see them.

Laughing, I told him that somebody might if there was a sudden gust of wind. Or if, worse still, I were to fall over – in which case, I would look quite the harlot.

Then he wondered what I might put on my feet. Going to my wardrobe, I showed him some black, flat shoes, with a wide toe. They didn't look so different to men's boots, I said, so I keep them with the others, telling him that I would put them on last. Next up were the petticoats: I had to tell him to stop stroking them. He replied that they 'must be unbearably *uncomfortable*, with all that horse-hair', giving them a longing look as he handed them to me. They won't touch my skin, I told him. Sadly, I could not say the same for the things on my chest, which I knew would itch unbearably.

I put on the petticoats, ensuring that they would give my lower body the right shape. Then I picked up the dress, shook it to straighten it out, and unlaced it at the back. I stepped into it and pulled it up to my shoulders, remarking on how low-cut it was as I put my hands through the sleeves. Simon laughed, saying that the frills around these arms made me 'look a little whore!' He went on to say that I would have to make sure it did not drop down over my chest, or people would think that I was entirely without modesty.

I put on my wig and brushed it in the mirror. After several attempts, I felt satisfied with the style, but I moved it several times, worried that people might not think it natural. Simon stood behind me and gently pulled it into place, smiling and running his hand through the hair. I looked at how all of my skin between my neck and my hands was covered in lace and satin, my eyes emboldened by all the shadow and mascara, the curls falling just above my eyebrows. Then I told him that I had spent all morning shaving, and that the overall effect was *marvellous*.

Simon told me that I 'should have worn less rouge', but that otherwise, I looked 'quite the lady'. I asked him if he meant it, and he replied: 'I'd marry you!' Those words that I had dreamed of hearing for so long! I threw my arms around him and said: '*I'd marry you too!*'

He told me not to kiss his cheek because I would get lipstick on it, so I went for his lips. He laughed, but I wanted him to let the moment last for longer. Undeterred, I put on my bonnet, and exclaimed: 'Now, my *husband* – let us go to the theatre!'

I paused, listening out for any voices, footsteps, doors opening and closing. I asked if he could hear anyone on the staircases; Simon insisted that we were safe. I wanted him to check, so he opened the door and looked around. The going was good, he assured me, taking my hand.

*

We stepped outside. Suddenly I became aware of the breeze pushing my frock against my legs, shooting up my skirt; of how much my boobies were not quite the right shape, and how many people might be staring. I worried about my wig blowing away, as nobody would be convinced by my hair, cut shorter last week after some choice remarks from the landlady. I tried to hold my head up and act as naturally as one could in such garb.

Simon asked if I knew any of my neighbours. I told him that I could not distinguish any of them from Adam, saying that I came to know enough of my neighbours back in Copthorne to last me a lifetime. A man walked past. He did not look at me until he brushed against my skirt. Then he gave me a glare, as if I had wronged him. I said nothing, and he carried on.

I said I was not sure that I would be able to sit through even the first act, referring to the whalebones in my corset. I asked how ladies did this, and *why*. Simon was clear: 'Because we make them.' When I said that you would think they would complain, he just replied that he was sure that they did.

Trying to ignore two passing men focused on my chest, I told Simon that everyone was looking at me.

'Do you want to be seen?' he replied.

I took Simon's arm, saying that I would rather be left alone, and that perhaps we should stay at home. He could not believe that I wanted to abandon the ship at this point. I did not want to, honestly, but I did not know whether to stick to the back-streets or try to blend in. Trying to reassure me, Simon suggested that we should take a cab. The driver would probably not notice anything strange about me, he said, but if he did, we could throw him a few more pennies.

We hired a hackney-carriage from Great Peter-street. A gentleman and his wife over-heard Simon telling the cab driver to take us to Drury-lane, and said they should like to ride with us, as they were also going to the theatre. I tugged at Simon's jacket, but he just said that it would save us a penny or two. He gave me a look to suggest there was nothing we could do to stop them riding with us, and that I would do best to keep quiet.

'A night at the theatre, is it?' said the man. Simon nodded. 'A rare treat for you, madam?'

What did he mean by this? I thought to myself. *Had I dressed like a pauper?* I just smiled, and he went on about a Christopher Marlowe production that he'd seen somewhere. I kept nodding, thinking that this insufferable bore's monologue would mean, at least, that he wouldn't be looking at my waist and thinking it might be too big, that my hands were a little too large, or that my Adam's apple might be visible. I put one hand on the other and held my head down.

'How long have you two been married?' he suddenly asked.

Yearning for our brief moment in my lodgings, I stumbled for an answer. Before I found one, Simon told him that 'we were betrothed three years ago', and I clasped my hands in the hope that our interlocuter would not look for a ring.

The man wished us a wonderful night, and all the happiness in the world. 'I must say,' he continued, looking at me. 'You don't speak much, do you?'

'A good lady knows to speak only when she is spoken to,' replied Simon, smiling and looking at the man's wife. 'Don't you agree?'

'I'm not sure that I do,' she answered. 'But such are the times.'

I'd never really thought about when or how to speak, I realised as the words passed her lips. I felt a little hopeless, and watched as she twisted her ring, pointedly looking away from her husband and out of the window. Simon asked the wretched man about other plays he had seen, and of course he had no hesitation in telling us, at great length. I kept quiet, trying not to speak and not to shake, and I practically skipped out of the carriage when we pulled up outside the theatre. The one good thing about this dullard's presence was that he offered to pay our fare, which seemed the least he could do. Thankfully, he was going to a private box, and we made our way inside without him.

*

Simon bought tickets from the box-keeper, and I was surprised to learn that I had to leave my bonnet with the woman at the entrance, giving her a penny for the privilege. I removed it with care, terrified that I would disturb my wig, but she didn't seem to notice, and if she *did*, she mercifully kept her thoughts to herself.

Then we took our seats in the Upper Circle. My petticoats

made my skirt so wide; I felt like a cat using its whiskers to get through a fence. I could sense that people were staring at me; as we had arrived early, I kept having to stand so that others could take their seats. As I pulled up my skirts to prevent them from being trodden upon, I saw people looking at my dress, and worried. *Had I worn too much crinoline? Had I painted my face too heavily?* One gentleman winked at me. *Did he know?*

I smiled and sat down. Soon, the curtain rose, and I stopped feeling so anxious – nobody would look at me once the play started, after all. I noticed soon after it commenced that I desperately needed to use the washroom, but I didn't know if they even had one for ladies. After all, I had barely seen any ladies there.

I looked around during the interval, but before I could find one, the man came up to Simon and asked a question.

'Excuse me, sir,' he said. 'Is this lady … your wife?'

'Oh, no,' Simon replied. 'We are just acquaintances on a night out.'

'She is tremendously pretty,' he continued, 'with all these curls.'

I put one hand on my head in the hope that he would not touch my wig. Worse; he took my other hand and kissed it. My first instinct was that Simon might be jealous; then I saw somebody glaring at me as I tugged on Simon's coat-tails. *People might think I'm soliciting,* I worried, and I thought it best to return to the theatre. The man wished us a pleasant evening; we simply smiled and went back inside.

During the second half, I noticed a man by the door, eyeing me suspiciously. I tried to ignore him, but every time I glanced back, he was there. I wondered if we should leave, but we would have disturbed the patrons, and I hoped that if we left with the crowd, we might avoid detection.

We stepped out of the theatre. Two constables were waiting. They grabbed my arm, and one of them asked if I was 'Peter Jordan of Rochester-row'.

'What?' I said, trying to affect my most feminine tone. 'Of course not! I'm–'

Then I stopped, realising that there likely *was* no 'Peter Jordan of Rochester-row', and that I had fallen straight into their trap.

'No, you're a man in female attire,' said the Bobby. 'You're coming with me,' he continued, laughing. Then he turned to Simon. 'Are you with him?'

I stopped almost dead, praying that Simon would stick to our script. Thankfully, he did, telling them that we had made a wager that I couldn't get through the performance undetected, 'for a lark'.

'It's always a bloody *lark*, isn't it?' said the constable, arresting Simon with me. They marched us to Bow-street Police Station. It took just a couple of minutes but felt like an eternity, with crowds around the pubs and the theatres staring at me, pointing and laughing. I was so hot that my make-up was coming off, but I wouldn't let the policeman take off my wig, and besides, I was more bothered about the pain in my back. Luckily, I didn't see anyone familiar, but I am not sure that they would have recognised me anyhow.

'Why did you go to Drury-lane?' asked the policeman as we turned onto Bow-street and saw the station. 'It's as if you *wanted* to come here.'

'And *why* all that crinoline?' said his friend, laughing.

'Sometimes I wonder if you *want* to get caught,' whispered Simon. Then we were separated.

*

Wednesday, 1ˢᵗ April, 1846.

This report was published in the *Times* this morning:

Yesterday a young man, in women's clothes, with short, brown hair, named George Watson, whose general demeanour denoted respectability of position, was placed at the bar before Mr. Green, where he was charged with frequenting the streets in female attire, and for a supposed unlawful purpose. This was the third or fourth case of its kind to be heard by the court in recent weeks, exposing a vice that threatens to become endemic to the capital.

Police constable B 77 said that the prisoner had been apprehended at the Drury-lane Theatre on Friday evening, during a performance of *Twelfth Night*, accompanied by a gentleman named Robert Hopkins. Asked if he had seen the prisoner before, B 77 stated that he had not, but that he had read recent reports about other such men, and could only conclude that the prisoner was similarly engaged in practices of the most unnatural character, possibly to obtain money.

There was much laughter in the court-room as B 77 described the prisoner's appearance, especially the bits of cloth knitted inside some pink wool to make a breast and the whale-bone in the corset discovered when the prisoner was stripped at the station, saying that it was the crinoline that induced him to notice the defendant. Asked the reason for being so dressed, the prisoner said that it had been 'a lark' and that Hopkins had bet him that he could not 'pass' undetected in his disguise.

Mr. Green remarked that in the absence of any further evidence, the prisoner's excuse would have to be accepted, although on top of whatever forfeit he would have to pay Mr. Hopkins after losing their bet, he would also have to furnish two sureties of 25*l.* each, to be of good behaviour for six months, or to be committed in default. The prisoner could only blame himself for this, said Mr. Green, as well as for any loss of position or earnings that resulted.

The prisoner held up his skirts, stepped out of the dock and retired, to the disquiet of the court.

Thinking back to his aside about *wanting* to get caught, I told Simon that it had been worth it, and that I would do it again. 'Not with me, you won't,' he said, half-laughing but I knew that he meant it. I said that perhaps we should keep it to the shop, as a compromise, but from the way he shrugged his shoulders and smiled, I couldn't be sure if he would return.

A WO/MAN OF NO IMPORTANCE

This pamphlet, subtitled 'Recollections of A. Parr', recounts events around the Oscar Wilde trial and London's decadent literary and artistic circles, and was recently found in an archive at University College London. Its author is yet to be identified; we can guess that it was not any of the writers or artists referenced within, but it is not confirmed whether it was written by a contributor to The Yellow Book[1]. It has a date – 1914 – so we know it was written with twenty years' hindsight. Perhaps the author believed that the start of the First World War would mean a relaxation (at least unofficially) of the Labouchere Amendment to the Criminal Law Amendment Act 1885, which made 'gross indecency' between consenting adults, public or private, punishable by two years' imprisonment with hard labour; or that this text might help to change the oppressive climate generated by Wilde's conviction. There is no evidence, however, that it was ever circulated, as doing so could have meant its publisher being charged with distributing obscene material, and there is little proof that Arthur Parr existed, although the ten-year-old recorded under that name in the Ardwick district of Manchester in the 1881 census is most likely its protagonist. The author's aim in writing this account, we can assume, was to ensure that Parr was not lost to history altogether.

I first met Arthur Parr on a winter afternoon in December 1894 or January 1895. Brought to me at a lavish dinner in Bloomsbury, I momentarily mistook him for someone else. The same long, flowing, dark hair, that cannot have curled so much without artifice; the same *debonair* mannerisms, even holding his cigarette in a similar fashion; the same style of frock-coat and velvet blazer. As soon as I realised that he must be nearly twenty years younger, I wondered if Parr had modelled himself on photographs of Oscar Wilde. The first thing he asked, in a broad Mancunian accent that

1 *The Yellow Book* was a quarterly periodical, edited by Henry Harland and published by John Lane and Elkin Mathews at The Bodley Head (London) from 1894-97.

offended the sensibilities of our more refined diners, was if anyone could introduce him to Oscar. It still pains me to admit that my next thought, as I listened to his long list of people with whom he hoped to become acquainted, was that this young man almost certainly meant trouble. The ease with which the names left his tongue – Edward Carpenter and Havelock Ellis amongst them – left little doubt about which topics he wished to discuss, and his tone made me feel that he wouldn't be doing so with much discretion. Such an impetuous youth, barely twenty-three, demanding an audience with some of the best minds of his generation – and insistent that he would become the brightest of their company!

All evening, Parr told anyone who would listen that he was 'a writer' whose plays, prose and poetry would eclipse even those of Shakespeare, 'and also an artist' whose drawings and paintings would scandalise Paris, let alone London. Such things may be a little way ahead of him, publisher Elkin Matthews told me a few days later, but Parr had submitted a handful of poems to *The Yellow Book* and whilst the editor, Henry Harland, had not felt them fit for publication, he liked them, seeing the influence of Rimbaud in their youthful idealism, Mallarmé in their dense symbolism, and Huysmans in their sordid self-disgust. So, they encouraged Parr to keep writing, and to meet his contemporaries; he asked me to introduce Parr to Aubrey Beardsley – a young man of his age. Beardsley and he soon became close, but Parr was more interested in sexual scientists like Ellis than artists. It took him some time to realise that the two were not so distinct; and rather longer to learn the need to be careful about which elements to bring into his work.

Parr had already read everything that Wilde had published and was soon introduced to his idol – via Beardsley, who had illustrated *Salomé*, rather than the publishers of *The Yellow Book*, which Wilde had dismissed as 'dull and loathsome'. Intrepid, Parr quizzed Oscar extensively about his work on their very first meeting, over a meal in Soho that deserved a far larger audience. (A shame, maybe, that Parr's questions didn't prepare Wilde for court.) Parr was so pleased with himself for identifying what he said was a brilliant allusion in *The Importance of Being Earnest*, then in its final rehearsals, to the trial of Ernest 'Stella' Boulton and Frederick 'Fanny' Park.[2] 'If Boulton is "Ernest" then he walks free; if she's "Stella" then she goes to gaol,' he declared to the guests at a dinner near *The Yellow Book* offices on Vigo Street a few days later. That the dandyish Cecil Graham in *Lady Windermere's Fan* took his name from the one that Boulton gave to the police on his arrest, said Parr, was proof that his theory was correct, although Oscar was too shrewd to offer anything so vulgar as clarification.

*

Within a few weeks, Parr had met *The Yellow Book*'s leading lights, and it seemed inevitable that he would appear within its pages. He had also met Carpenter and Ellis, who showed him a passage in Richard von Krafft-Ebing's *Psychopathia Sexualis*, about a woman with a morbid aversion to female attire, who wanted nothing more than to live as her beloved's husband. Parr was excited by this, and by a scurrilous novel

---

2 Ernest 'Stella' Boulton (1847-1904) and Frederick 'Fanny' Park (1846-1881) were cross-dressers, arrested in London in April 1870 under suspicion of being part of a cross-class sodomite ring. They were tried for 'inciting others to commit unnatural offences', amidst great public interest; after six days, they were acquitted.

by 'Viscount Ladywood' about a young man forced into cross-sexed servitude by a house of ladies, though I never heard him talk about women – just their clothing. When I read *The Intermediate Sex* by Edward Carpenter, on its publication six years ago, there was one passage that instantly struck me as a perfect description of Parr: 'A distinctly effeminate type, sentimental, lackadaisical, mincing in gait and manners, something of a chatter-box, skilful at the needle and in women's work, sometimes taking pleasure in dressing in women's clothes; his figure not unfrequently betraying a tendency towards the feminine ... while his dwelling-room is orderly in the extreme, even natty, and choice of decoration and perfume. His affection, too, is often feminine in character, clinging, dependent and jealous, as of one desiring to be loved almost more than to love.'

Parr spent as much time as he could with the two scientists, and naturally, he soon offered to help them with their research. There were many ways he could have done this, I am sure; but he was determined that the best was to find people to attend a men-only fancy-dress ball, to be held at a secret location in London, and along the way, introduce them to Carpenter and Ellis.

Immediately, people tried to persuade Parr of the folly of this. He was convinced, though, that his party could evade the law; and that even should it fail, that the defences of the past would protect him in the present. At another *Yellow Book* dinner, attended by many of the journal's greatest poets and painters, authors and illustrators, the subject was the matter of considerable debate. In truth, most of the guests – particularly Lane and Mathews – would have preferred not to discuss it at all, anxious about the possibility of word reaching the wrong ears, but Parr, as usual, would not be derailed. Bringing up the most famous legal precedent, Parr reminded everyone that Boulton and Park won their freedom by arguing that their female personas were extensions of their theatrical roles, while laughing at the very idea that a 'medical inspection' could prove *anything*. Then, he spoke at length about a ball held at the Temperance Hall in Hulme, Manchester, in September 1880. He said that he had known one of its participants. There had been fifty people there, Parr recited; they had made sure that nothing 'unnameable' was visible, covering all windows that could be seen into from the street or neighbouring buildings, with entry only by password. They had even hired a blind organist to play *The Can-Can*.

'That didn't stop them getting raided, did it?' said Ernest Dowson, dismissively.

'Perhaps not,' Parr replied, smiling. 'Although they put up a hell of a fight, given their dress. I wouldn't be so complacent as to leave *any* window without blinds, no matter how hard it might be to peer through. Anyway, their lawyers said that to convict them for 'a vice so hateful that it could not be named amongst Christians' would 'bring shame to all of Manchester'. And of course, the court couldn't have *that*.'

'They got off?' asked Beardsley.

'Twenty-five pounds in fines, and an order to be of good behaviour for a year.' (At this point, I wondered if Parr might be capable of such behaviour for a week, let alone a year; and given his lack of any discernible occupation, a twenty-five-pound fine would be ruinous.)

'And their names in all the newspapers,' added Harland. 'What happened to your friend after he handed over his money?' Parr fell silent. 'Did he just become some ne'er-do-well?'

'He moved from Salford to Fallowfield. He worked under an assumed name but seemed happy enough to me. Anyway, one is always allowed more freedom if one is a *great artist.*'

'You didn't hear about Luke Limner, then?' said John Lane. 'They found him on the highway and made him stand in the dock in a ridiculous hat and high-heels. He said that he was an artist, writing a book on female attire, and needed personal experience to treat the subject properly. They still fined him five pounds.'

'Perhaps they fined him for making such *terrible* work,' Parr retorted, his face dropping as he saw nobody else laughing. 'Besides, five pounds is nothing!' he insisted. 'We can cover that.'

'*We?*' asked Lane.

'What about Edward Hamblar?' interjected Walter Sickert, breaking Parr's silence. 'The police caught him in Bromley Street, dressed as a woman. The crowd were going to tear him to pieces – they thought he was the Ripper. He was lucky to escape with a £10 fine!'

'Whoever Jack was, it's over now,' replied Parr. 'And both of your subjects made the mistake of going out in public. I would keep things behind closed doors.'

'Things have changed,' replied Sickert. 'That's no longer sufficient!'

Before Parr could answer, in walked Max Beerbohm. He broke the news that the Marquess of Queensberry, furious about Wilde's relationship with his son Alfred Douglas (or 'Bosie'), had been barred from the opening night of *The*

Importance of Being Earnest. Undeterred, he had sought out Wilde at the Albemarle Club. After being refused entry, he had left a card for 'Oscar Wilde, posing somdomite' *[sic]*. We did not yet know what would arise, but shortly afterwards, Wilde had consulted a solicitor, and Queensberry was arrested for criminal libel.

*

If Parr's fancy-dress ball had been a bad idea before, it was a terrible one now. What little of the night was not spent discussing Wilde's wisdom in pursuing Queensberry through the courts was used on talking Parr out of *his* scheme. That effort, at least, was not wasted. He decided, instead, to pen a short story about just such an occasion, basing his work on what he had heard about the Temperance Hall. He promised to write under a pseudonym, aware that publishing his piece in this way could still draw people to him; by doing so, he claimed, his work would help 'inverts', and thus fulfil a similar function to that of Carpenter or Ellis.

Even this idea met with considerable scepticism, but Parr went on with his manuscript anyway. Two weeks later, he came back with five thousand words, which began with a beautiful young man who planned to escape his overwhelming feelings of disgust and detachment by organising a magnificent festival, where men became women and women became men, first by adopting the clothing of the opposite sex, and then, through a fantastical process only known to occur in this 'sacred' space, transforming their bodies for one heavenly night. He was much encouraged by Beardsley, whose fantastical romantic novel *Under the*

Hill had a protagonist who wore silk stockings and garters (and whose escapades were severely curtailed when Lane eventually published the unfinished manuscript, nearly ten years later). Parr told anyone within earshot that his work was quite unique. In this, he was right. Harland, Lane and Mathews read his story and instantly feared a greater scandal than the one caused by *The Picture of Dorian Gray*. Sounding more surprised than they probably should, given Parr's earlier declaration that his work would generate exactly that, they said they could not possibly include it within *The Yellow Book*'s pages – or, at least, not without him completely rewriting it.

Furious, Parr asked the worth of editors who 'butcher their meat so badly that they only ever serve offal'; their suggestion that he use their press to print and distribute it anonymously only enraged him further. He had not, he said, written 'some two-bit titillation like *The Sins of the Cities of the Plain*'[3]; in France, he yelled, 'even such a philistine as *[Maurice]* Barrès'[4] would recognise his story as a work of genius'. They told him that their friends were advising Wilde against prosecuting Queensberry, and instead to move to Paris. Knowingly or not, Parr then echoed Oscar's line about learning who one's true friends are at such moments; I felt Lane and Mathews generous in telling him to tread carefully, and then making their excuses. When I asked him about it the next day, Lane was far more forgiving than I might have been, saying only that similar arguments had occurred before with other authors, and doubtless would again.

---

3 *The Sins of the Cities of the Plain; or, The Recollections of a Mary-Ann, with Short Essays on Sodomy and Tribadism* was an erotic novel about a rent boy's experiences, published by 'Jack Saul' in 1881.
4 Maurice Barrès (1862-1923) was a right-wing French poet, journalist and politician, associated with Symbolism, especially Italian proto-Fascist author Gabriele D'Annunzio.

*

Meanwhile, Arthur – or Anthea, as he had taken to calling himself – had become less focused on publishing his story, and more intent on living it. I first met 'Anthea' at a soirée on a spring evening in March 1895. I wondered if Parr had arrived so dressed to make a point about our men-only policy, but then remembered that, in all truth, our gatherings were *always* men-only, and the only difference tonight was that it had been made official. Perhaps, then, it was to spite Lane and Mathews. But this was not a *Yellow Book* event, and they did not attend. No: Parr was now referring to himself as an 'invert', explaining the concept as Carpenter and Ellis had outlined it, and demanded that we refer to him by this new name. This felt like a huge step, but within reach, as Parr looked resplendent with her hair twisted into a coil atop her head, in rouge and deep red lipstick. I guessed that her gown had come from Paris, with its low neck and high sleeves, in sky-blue decorated with lace – the absolute epitome of the *Belle Epoque*.

Parr had set herself against her publisher, and apart from her contemporaries; the nervousness about the presence of a latter-day Stella Boulton was palpable. At first, the only person willing to entertain her was Carpenter, despite his oft-stated discomfort around the more effeminate creatures who came his way. I saw them in a corner, ensconced in dialogue, and at one point, Carpenter took Parr's hands and started to implore her. Perhaps he was telling her about Alfred Taylor and Arthur Marling's recent arrest for wearing female attire to John Watson Preston's club at 46 Fitzroy-street. Years later, when I read Carpenter's passage in *The*

Intermediate Sex on the Criminal Law Amendment Act and its 'censorship over private morals', my mind retracted to that night. Indeed, I can still recall the way Parr's expression darkened on hearing about Taylor and Marling.

Later, I saw Parr dance with Beardsley and Dowson, with a fair few watching suitors – not least Sickert, whose gaze was contemptuous. Anthea spoke so delicately, moved so freely and danced so gracefully that I almost forgot, not just our anxieties about Oscar – about to abandon his case against Queensberry rather than call Bosie as a witness – but also that as far as we were concerned, this was Anthea's first night in the world. Then, I felt Parr might do well to abandon writing and take up female impersonation. Word had reached us that after his acquittal in 1871, 'Stella' had moved to the United States and launched a new career as Ernest Byne. To the thrill of Parr – and everyone else present – Beardsley had acquired a magnificent photograph, which showed 'Byne' as a high-society lady in a beautiful hat and frock-coat. Inspired, Parr asked how he might contact 'Stella', and I began to think that having her out of London, and the United Kingdom, might prove better for everyone.

Soon, all were assured that Parr's future lay in impersonation, if not on the stage (as he still seemed too coarse for a role written by Ibsen or Shaw, let alone Marlowe or Shakespeare), then at least in the music hall. Perhaps, in trying to rid our party of him, men lined up to tell Parr of friends in the theatre – actors, directors, impresarios – who could help. Within days, Parr had arranged meetings, and talked beforehand of stage routines, jokes to tell, and songs to sing. He returned from each encounter empty-handed, however. As Wilde's libel suit collapsed and he and Alfred

Taylor (who, it turned out, had owned a male brothel) were charged under the Criminal Law Amendment Act and taken to Holloway Prison, Parr found no theatre willing to associate itself with an 'invert', even if, like Stella, he promised to draft his mother into any potential court case to explain that his masquerade was a harmless game that had persisted since childhood. A move to Paris or New York looked best, and we soon met to discuss it.

*

Parr, as we all knew by now, was not built for life's practicalities, and the necessary work to move across an ocean was beyond him. He could find the money for a ball-gown to be worn once in a lifetime, but not for even a third-class travel ticket; he could impress himself upon London literary circles with seemingly no effort at all, but the idea of meeting new people in another country apparently petrified him. Nobody was willing to lend money to someone so unlikely to repay it, even if he remained in our city, and as the final trial of Wilde and Taylor began, few of us felt able to concentrate on Parr, who – miraculously – had not yet attracted such nefarious attention. Indeed, Lane and Mathews' principal concern was in dissociating themselves from Oscar; given his well-known disdain for their publication, they resented the attention that resulted from reports that Wilde had carried a copy on his arrest when his 'yellow book' was actually a French edition of Pierre Louÿs' *Aphrodite* (which, like most of the French literature that Wilde enjoyed, had a simple yellow cover). Parr was livid when they sacked Beardsley as *The Yellow Book*'s art editor and removed his drawings from the April 1895 issue, even though they only did so after literary figures publicly lambasted them and their office windows were smashed. He was even angrier when they returned his manuscript, insisting that they could never claim knowledge of it in court, and advised that he destroy every copy.

This suggestion, and the impossibility of relocation, only seemed to spur Parr further along a dangerous path, despite the revelation that the police had found plenty of women's clothing at Alfred Taylor's rooms on Little College-street, which would likely be used as evidence against him and Wilde. Once again, Parr was unperturbed – the discovery of a house on Wakefield-street where Boulton and Park had stored their theatrical inventory had not served to convict them, and this news would not prevent him from organising the party of his dreams. I urged Carpenter, who seemed like the only person to whom Parr might listen, to step in, but what more could he say? Clearly, Parr's mind was made up, and the best option for everyone else was to shield themselves from the inevitable explosion: Lane gave him strict instructions not to associate any of this activity with *The Yellow Book*. (In any case, by now, many contributors were scathing, and Beerbohm's admonishment was especially harsh: 'How are you going to find your attendees? By placing a notice in *The Times*?') Now, Parr was practically alone, having just the increasingly tubercular Beardsley for moral support.

*

Several people whom Parr hoped could help were involved with the trial, and I counselled him to stay away from them.

He particularly wanted to track down Preston, even after learning that Preston dabbled in blackmail, and seemed unconcerned that the police might still be monitoring the Fitzroy-street premises. He eventually *did* arrange a private meeting with Preston, who thought his plans unwise, but nonetheless put him in touch with John Severs, a tobacconist's assistant who had lost his income after appearing in court (in female attire) for his part in the previous year's ball, but had, like the other defendants, escaped gaol. Severs did not want to attend Parr's event – a second judge might not prove so lenient – but knew a few people who would, and who would also know a few others who would. Before long, Parr had a small circle of co-conspirators, and could now begin his search for a venue.

One of the group had a family friend who ran a hotel in Aldgate. They would not disclose their real purpose, they agreed, but tell the proprietor that they were holding a party after a wedding. (As it transpired, this contained a glint of truth.) Otherwise, Parr applied all his learning from the Temperance Hall. Entry would be allowed only by password (using the same one – 'Sister') and the pianist, recommended by Severs, would be a man of poor eyesight. Unlike his predecessors in Manchester, Parr ensured that *every* window was covered, and that they had an obvious escape plan, to be explained to everyone who gave the password. They had a code-word ('Cromwell') for a raid; if it were yelled, they would leave via the fire exit, race down the spiral staircase and head east.

Parr had wanted to make illustrated invites, but Beardsley was too busy, and worried about making himself ill. Beardsley would at least attend, though, and might incorporate certain scenes into future works if he felt so inspired. Having listened to all this, I had to admit my curiosity. *The Yellow Book* organised a dinner in Bloomsbury, doubtless to give themselves an alibi if Parr and his cohort ended up on trial; I chose to go to the ball, despite hearing via a friend that Taylor been cross-examined in court that morning about having 'a woman's dress', wig and stockings in his rooms, his presence at Fitzroy-street, and his lack of occupation, but mostly about his interest in young men. I had no desire to wear female attire, then or at any other time, but I wanted to see how close Parr's reality came to his fantasy.

The Cumberland Hotel could never live up to the distant, star-lit plains of Parr's story, and in truth, nor could most of the attendees. There were about twenty-five – an impressive number, given the understandable reticence of Parr's invitees – although their costumes proved a huge let-down. (I know mine did: the cheapest suit in my possession, chosen more because it was the most amenable to a hasty exit than for any stylistic reason.) There were just a handful of people in female attire, with the 'ladies' outnumbered by more than two to one, and potential suitors further disappointed as two of the ladies danced only with each other. Most were not convincing, either because they were too tall or too broad, or dressed in a fashion fifty years past, in corsets that did little to hide their masculine girth; or in one case, sporting lipstick and rouge around a thick, brown beard and moustache, which, s/he said, 'my wife will not let me shave.' A couple, however, may have kept up their deception for long enough to have some genuine larks. Certainly, I was momentarily taken in; a few more whiskies, and who knows where an honest gentleman might have been led!

Parr, of course, spared no expense in making himself a work of art, and was never in danger of being upstaged. He had purchased a new dress with even higher sleeves and an even lower neck, adorned with roses, worn with silk gloves and stockings. (Where he found it, let alone how he paid for it, remains a mystery.) 'Anthea' was the last attendee to enter, to applause, whistles and Wagner's *Bridal Chorus*; one gentleman, unfamiliar to me, threw a bouquet at her feet and took her hand. After much revelry, the music stopped. The guests began to cheer and clap, and a man in a suit walked onto the floor to tell everyone that we were gathered here tonight to celebrate the holy matrimony between Miss Anthea Parr and … *Cromwell!*

One attendee must have been an informer, and may have spent the night noting the names and faces of his fellow guests. (It may even have been someone associated with *The Yellow Book,* although I hope not.) Later, I learned that the Manchester revellers had borrowed 'sister' from previous balls, which had allowed the police to guess the password and gain access to the Temperance Hall and made it even more reckless for Parr to use it, but maybe nobody had told him so. In any case, I had sensibly, if not courageously, spent much of my evening by the fire escape. I hurried down the stairs, not looking back as I ran all the way to the London Hospital. I saw Beardsley struggling after me: I sometimes wonder how many years those few seconds took off his life, but he did escape that night, down Leman-street and then to who knows where, but as *The Picture of Dorian Gray* had led us to expect, the police did not follow us into the depths of Whitechapel. Parr, in her corset and long silk train, was not so nimble, nor so lucky.

*

At Marlborough-street, Parr was charged on remand with being idle and disorderly in Aldgate, and with being in female attire for the purpose of inciting acts of gross indecency, under the Criminal Law Amendment Act. Privately, we held great discussion about whether Carpenter or Ellis should testify in Parr's favour, or at least plead for clemency, and how they might do this without bringing literary London into further disrepute. (Fortunately, the police had not identified Beardsley as one of the attendees.) Parr went to the dock still wearing his gown, his corset and train removed, his hair now far from perfect, his lipstick barely visible and his unshaved facial hair sprouting. He was a sorry sight, as the court took great pleasure in pointing out; they also laughed at his accent, which veered between his native Mancunian, as he hoped that the court might not trouble itself too much with a Northern vagabond, and the affectations of our crowd, as he struggled to convince them of his 'good character'. This fooled nobody, as the wealthier patrons – of whom the police had managed to apprehend just three – all agreed that Parr had been solely responsible for the party's organisation, and that he had tricked them into coming. (The near-blind pianist, in the witness box, affirmed this.)

Parr trembled as the prosecuting lawyer, Mr. Wynyard, cross-examined him about who were his patrons for the ball, how he found them, and whether he had organised such a thing before. He denied the latter, sounding plausible because it was true, but then Wynyard produced a wad of papers, passed on by the police after they searched his room for women's clothing, and which I immediately recognised as enough to condemn him.

Asked if he was a writer, Parr replied balefully that he had no occupation, and lived off money from his father's cotton mill in Ancoats, Manchester. Asked if he wrote, Parr hesitated, and then said, 'I dabble.' Shorn of his previous swagger, he did not talk as the lawyer read long extracts from his unpublished and unpublishable manuscript. The scenes of drunken jubilation when the men transformed into women, and submitted to the women who temporarily became men, drew gasps from the jury; Wynyard's question about 'whether there existed a periodical in the land who might even consider publishing such obscenity' drew only silence from Parr.

Then came an attendee, Eric Broughton, who had agreed to testify against Parr. When Wynyard read the scene from Parr's story 'about a wedding between two men', Broughton detailed the ceremony at the Cumberland Hotel, where 'Anthea' had given her hand to Lord Rawlinson-Page, a fifty-two-year-old former General and aristocrat who had recently inherited a fortune, and whom Parr had hoped would provide financial support. Rawlinson-Page had escaped on the night and immediately sailed to France, and could not be traced. Broughton knew nothing else of their relationship; given Parr's propensity to boast about almost anything, I was surprised that I had never heard about it, and neither had any of our associates.

Unlike the trial of Wilde and Taylor, there were no young men brought to stand, to my relief. Parr's lawyer tried to argue that whilst he should have known better, being highly intelligent (and clearly of great imagination), his actions simply youthful folly, which he would surely not repeat after this public humiliation. Parr had an interest in the theatre, they said, especially Shakespeare – unusual for someone of his background – and it was this that had animated him, and nothing more sinister. For his story, however, they struggled to account, making a more general argument about the dangers of criminalising art, which was met with a counter-argument about the dangers of popularising smut. They concluded by appealing to the jury to consider the reputation of London, 'the jewel of the Empire', and not to blemish it by convicting their client of an offence for which there was little proof.

By this powerful speech, I was greatly moved. The judge, Goodhart, held firm. Too many such cases had reached court for them to turn a blind eye, he said, especially with legislation now able to stamp out the 'despicable vice' that threatened to overwhelm the city. He mentioned Wilde and Taylor, both convicted in a recent session, and remarked that 'decent men' should no more tolerate 'such depravity', and most certainly should not let it pass under the guise of theatre, literature or art. Those who had attended the ball in male clothing were fined £5 and warned to be of good behaviour for three months; those in female attire, £20 and twelve months.

That left only Parr. The leniency of the preceding sentences, coupled with the severity of the judge's remarks, made me anxious that he was going to be singled out, and so it happened. The manuscript and the wedding ceremony were enough for two years' penal servitude with hard labour, and he was taken to Pentonville Prison, where they apparently had strict orders to keep him away from Wilde and Taylor. (In any case, Wilde was soon moved to Reading.)

Staying in touch with anyone convicted under the Criminal Law Amendment Act was risky, and none of the *Yellow Book* contributors did. Just before Parr's release, Beardsley – the only one who maintained even sporadic contact – converted to Catholicism, renounced his drawings and writing and moved to the French Riviera in the hope of halting his physical deterioration. This proved unsuccessful, and Beardsley died in March 1898, two and a half years before his friend Oscar. Parr was broken by his time in gaol, and did not even achieve his hero's infamy. The judge may have had no reservations about staining the national character, but the newspapers did, feeling that the Wilde scandal had caused damage enough and providing minimal coverage – the *Standard* described him as 'an unsuccessful writer' in a brief court report, but I saw nothing else. I spent many sleepless nights thinking about whether to describe the proceedings as I saw them from my position in the public gallery, for a newspaper or elsewhere, wondering if Parr might *want* the notoriety of national coverage. I never asked him, though: I decided that if Parr had a *Ballad of Reading Gaol* or *De Profundis* in him, he could better write it himself. He never did.

After his release, Parr – still only twenty-seven – needed a long rest and a change of location. Three years too late, we finally managed to get him on a boat to New York, on a one-way, third-class ticket, using money provided by The Bodley Head. I never heard from him again, and dared to imagine that, like Boulton/Byne, he had successfully reinvented himself on the American stage. Four years later, a telegram arrived at John Lane's desk, telling us that instead, Parr had gone the way of Beardsley and Wilde, but with nothing so great as *Salomé* to show for it.

London, September 1914.

RECONFIGURATION

This paper was published in Issue 2, Volume 14 of the Journal of British Gender Studies in spring 2020. It was first presented at the Recovering Queer Lives conference at the University of Sussex on 31 May 2019.

....

ARCHIVE

Havelock Ellis, *Eonism* and Sexual Inversion: The emergence of female-to-male culture in inter-war Britain

CJ FERGUSON

Abstract *In this paper, CJ Ferguson discusses his research into the archives of eminent British sexologist Havelock Ellis (1859-1939) regarding* Eonism *(1928) – the first British work to focus exclusively on the phenomenon of gender variance. The author presents a previously unpublished case study that Ellis carried out in 1927-28, made up of Ellis's correspondence with other sexologists, and transcripts of conversations with an individual known only as R. Ferguson suggests that Ellis' inability to fit trans men into his intellectual framework accounts for* Eonism's *lack of contemporary impact, and subsequent obscurity. In doing so, Ferguson highlights the emergence of trans-masculine identities during the inter-war period, reclaiming such identities for people who might now think of themselves as trans men, who understood themselves as 'inverts' at the time but were later codified as lesbians, leading to gender-variant individuals being erased from historical accounts.*

Introduction

Although his work is no longer widely read, Havelock Ellis remains one of the most important figures in the history of British sexology. As well as working towards a greater understanding of homosexuality amidst the repression caused by the Criminal Law Amendment Act 1885 and the conviction of Oscar Wilde, Ellis was the first to take what we now call transgender behaviour seriously. German sexologist Magnus Hirschfeld made his influential distinction between gender variance and homosexuality in *The Transvestites: The Erotic Desire to Cross-Dress* (1910); eighteen years later, Ellis published *Eonism*, the first British book on the subject, as part of his six-volume *Studies in the Psychology of Sex*.

Believing that cross-gender behaviour sprang from an identification with, and imitation of, an object of desire, Ellis coined 'Eonism' after French spy, soldier, and diplomat Chevalier d'Éon, who lived in London as a woman from 1777 to 1810, and sought autobiographical testimonies to support his thesis. Completed as Hirschfeld's colleagues at the Institute of Sexual Science in Berlin were working towards the first sex reassignment surgeries, *Eonism* opened with a curiously timid reiteration of Hirschfeld's pioneering distinction, explaining that 'Many years ago, when exploring the phenomenon of sexual inversion *[in* Sexual Inversion *[1898] and* Sexo-Aesthetic Inversion *(1913)]* I was puzzled by occasional cases ... of people who took pleasure in behaving and dressing like the opposite sex and yet were not sexually inverted.'[1] The text focused on cross-dressers for whom there was 'usually no real primary inversion *[and]* no true fetishism *[sic]*' about clothing, focusing primarily on

---

1 Ellis, H. (1936) 'Eonism and Other Supplementary Studies' in *Studies in the Psychology of Sex, Vol. III, Part Two*. New York: Random House, p1.

its subjects' attitudes to gender.[2] Crucially, he wrote that, 'On the psychic side, as I view it, the Eonist is embodying, in an extreme degree, the aesthetic attitude of imitation of, and identification with, the admired object. It is normal for a man to identify himself with the woman he loves. The Eonist carries that identification too far, stimulated by a sensitive and feminine element in himself which is associated with a rather defective virile sexuality on what may be a neurotic basis.'[3]

Whilst wishing to move beyond his previous ideas about 'inversion', Ellis remained convinced that 'homosexuality always seems primary' in female-to-male cross-dressers, which may account for the lack of female-to-male voices in *Eonism*.[4] The published volume included a brief discussion of British Army surgeon James Barry (1795-1865), found after death to have been assigned female at birth, and who apparently gave 'no indication of any sexual tendency … whether heterosexual or homosexual'[5]; it featured just one living female Eonist, who identified as a man only in dreams. Recent research into Ellis's papers, given by his adopted son François Lafitte to the British Library in 1988, has unearthed a far more complex study of a female-to-male individual, which did not make it into the final text, nor into Ellis's statements of support for Radclyffe Hall's novel *The Well of Loneliness* (1928) when it became the subject of an obscenity trial. Although he then published several more *Studies in the Psychology of Sex,* as well as his autobiography, Ellis did not return to the subject of 'Eonism', or make any public effort to apply his theory to female-to-male behaviour during the

---

2   Ibid., p11.
3   Ibid.
4   Ibid, p1.
5   Ibid., p6.

final decade of his life, for reasons that shall be explored in this paper.

Ellis and R.

On 4 February 1927, Ellis wrote to fellow sexologist Dr Norman Haire,[6] asking for help in finding 'more female Eonists ... who want to dress as, or be like men' to test his theory 'from the opposite direction' and help him 'to establish whether medical or psychological support would be most appropriate'. He wrote: 'I am more sympathetic to Dr. Hirschfeld's overall approach' (of asking people about their impulses and drawing conclusions from their statements) than that of Krafft-Ebing,[7] 'who believed cross-dressing a step 'on the road to insanity'' (and treated any correspondence on the matter accordingly), 'so you can assure anyone whom you refer to me that they will be met with the utmost sensitivity.'[8]

Haire sent 'the daughter of a friend in the medical profession, living in south Wales, who has always had a rather mannish demeanour' – this friend being a doctor, employed at St Mary's Hospital in Paddington, who had helped Haire to settle after his move from Australia to London. Haire expressed doubt over whether this person would be suitable, however, as 'she is inclined mainly towards women', although he added that 'she has been in a long-term relationship with a man ... so may still be of interest'.[9] This *was* of interest – perhaps *because* of this

---

6 Norman Haire, born Norman Zions (1892-1952), one of Britain's most prominent inter-war sexologists.

7 Richard von Krafft-Ebing (1840-1902), Austro-German psychiatrist, and author of *Psychopathia Sexualis* (1886). Although this book was aimed at psychiatrists, physicians, and judges, it popularised the terms 'Sadism' and 'Masochism', although Freud's idea that homosexuality was a psychological phenomenon eclipsed his theory of it as a biological anomaly.

8 Ellis to Haire, 4 February 1927.

9 Haire to Ellis, 9 February 1927.

sexual complexity, which differed from the other female-to-male people or female inverts who Ellis had met. He may not have known many: Ellis had used just six lesbian case histories in *Sexual Inversion*.[10]

Ellis's first notes on this daughter, recorded only as 'R.' are dated 16 March 1927.[11] They are part of a file that includes his correspondence with Haire, records on his own contributions to the dialogue (sometimes fully written up in the first person, in which case they are presented here as such; sometimes in a more fragmentary form, in which case I have worked them into the text) and direct transcripts of R.'s testimony, starting with the below:

'I was born in Cardiff, twenty-nine years ago, to parents who already had a three-year-old son, Clifford, and loved us both dearly. My father was a doctor, discussed in our area in the highest regard, and he met my mother when she was working as a medical secretary – she left her job when Cliff was born to devote herself to raising a family. My father worked long hours, and would sometimes go back to London, or elsewhere, for conferences, so I spent far more time with my mother, who took Cliff and me to Church every Sunday, and often read to me. My favourites were always the adventure stories that my father had bought for Cliff; I loved to imagine myself as the sea-captains or explorers in those books.

'Soon, I found that I wanted to dress like these characters, rather than like my father. He wanted Cliff to become a doctor too, and my parents gave Cliff an education not just in medicine,

---

10 Grosskurth, P. (1980) *Havelock Ellis: A Biography*. London: Allen Lane, p188.
11 All attempts to trace R. have, thus far, been unsuccessful. There is only one 'Clifford' listed as having died at Gallipoli with the South Wales Borderers, and he had no sisters, so it is likely that Ellis (or R.) used a pseudonym for R.'s brother. A search of the 1901, 1911 and 1921 censuses has not yielded anyone whose name begins with R. who fits the details in this case history, and so R.'s identity will probably remain a mystery. (Perhaps Ellis chose to use 'R.' as a coded reference to Radclyffe Hall – or, just as likely, to R's youthful choice of 'Robert'.) Although it may be an anachronism, we have opted for the gender-neutral pronoun *they* (singular) to describe R.

but also the arts. They were very proud that he was accepted into school at Cowbridge Grammar. Whenever I could, I wore his clothes – not just his uniform, although I wished I could have the schooling that he did, especially when I tried on his tie and blazer – but also his shirts and trousers. As a boy, I called myself Robert, and invented a life for myself, where I went to university, and then to sea, exploring the world with gay abandon. One time, my father came home early from watching a rugby match, and found me dressed as Robert. I thought he would be furious, but he just laughed and said that those clothes weren't for me. I think he thought I was just having some harmless fun.'

Ellis's transcript of R.'s dialogue included his interjections, which were mostly brief questions. Ellis noted that he asked what R. had been doing at this moment. When R. replied that 'I can't really remember. Having a day-dream about fighting pirates, I think,' Ellis pointed out that 'It's not unusual for little girls to want to be boys' and asked if R. had, as a child.

'It was merely a fantasy. Of course, I imagined what life might be like if I were to grow up to be a man – and why not fantasise about being the kind of man in those *Boy's Own* stories?'

'You admired the swash-buckling types, rather than the ones with humdrum jobs?' asked Ellis. R. laughed, affirmatively. 'Were those the kind of people you were attracted towards? Or did you imagine yourself as an adventurer with a beautiful wife?'

'I was too young to think about anything like that! In my fantasies, I was always in the company of men, crossing the Arctic or captaining a ship towards unchartered lands. My mother detested it when I acted like a young man – we would have fearful rows about the length of my hair, which I always wanted cut short. Eventually, I won that argument, but then my breasts started to develop, and I had bigger problems than what was on my head. I often grew angry, quickly, over very little, and she would tell me that wasn't how young ladies were supposed to behave, which just made it worse. At this point, I began to dream not only about being a man, but also about a young lady, Marianne, the daughter of my father's partner at his practice. She looked like a heroine from a Jane Austen novel – flowing, strawberry-blonde hair and the most feminine figure – and as soon as we met, I realised that everything I didn't want to be, I found desirable.'

Ellis asked about dreams: if R. was 'a man or a woman' in them, and if Marianne ever appeared.

'It was never clear … I was in my body, and very aware of that, but never of the clothes I was wearing, and in fact the whole world around me felt drained of colour and devoid of sound, as if I were trapped in a moving picture. I would be on a train, alone, looking for the conductor, as I feared that I had missed my stop. Whichever way I approached, his back was turned, and nothing persuaded him to face me. The train only moved faster, whistling as it hurtled through our stop, and I caught just a glimpse of Marianne sitting on the platform, looking as alone as I felt, but in her summer finery, her hair the most brilliant auburn, and usually, I woke up before the whistle blew and the engine smashed into a bricked-up tunnel.'

Ellis did not analyse this dream in any detail, saying only that its meaning was 'rather obvious'. Instead, he asked if R, had any dreams of being 'more masculine', or of intimacy with Marianne – and if they tended to occur simultaneously.

'Yes, but not as often as I wished. Just once, a fragment of a wedding. I have never cursed my body more for removing me from a fantasy as I did in that moment, in the middle of the night, and of course when I got back to sleep, it was unrecoverable … It was magnificent, but always so miserably fleeting.'

Ellis wrote in a letter to Haire that 'I told R. that the only other woman I had spoken to [about Eonism] experienced erotic dreams from the onset of sexual life, where she was a young man, making love to a woman.'[12] This was the only comparable case history that made the final text: 'a Welshwoman, twenty-nine years of age, married two years since' who was 'attractive to men, and attracted to them', and found the idea of homosexual affairs abhorrent.[13] Her husband 'had not even been aware that [she] needed arousing, or that anything beyond penetration and ejaculation was required'; once he realised that she also had erotic needs, learned to satisfy her 'almost, if not quite' as much as these dream sequences.[14] (At this point, Ellis considered the case study closed, and did not probe further.) Ellis already sensed that R.'s interest in women went far beyond dreams, privately lamenting his own 'inability to feel such strong and healthy passions'[15], and asked R. about 'how often these feelings extend into your waking hours'. As Ellis anticipated, R. emphatically rejected his implication that these desires sprang from a need for satisfaction from a male lover, or were confined to dreams:

---

12 Ellis to Haire, 21 March 1927.
13 Ellis, Eonism, p37.
14 Ibid., p40.
15 Ellis to Haire, 21 March 1927. Despite his lifelong dedication to sexology, Ellis's own aversion to intimacy was widely noted by his contemporaries, especially his companion, author and anti-war campaigner Olive Schreiner (1855-1920), who described Ellis as 'too idealistic for anything as earthy as sex'.

'I don't know why I felt like this – still thinking in my mind that I would like to meet a man and marry, and sometimes meeting men who I genuinely considered handsome, but in my heart, knowing that such a life was categorically not for me. My parents, my grandparents and my brother did not seem to feel this way, and I often wished that I could feel as comfortable as my mother, or Marianne – I wanted to tell her how much I adored her, but it always felt doomed. In any case, the news that Cliff had been killed at Gallipoli soon overshadowed this. My dreams intensified: I found myself on the front, rushing towards the German guns, a man not unlike my brother, or our friends in the South Wales Borderers who died with him, bolting awake when the bullet hit my heart ... And I wondered if my desire to be a man was a wish to replace him, my desire for Marianne a wish to have the family that he might have had ... and then I remembered that those dreams had been there for years.'

R.'s familial testimony anticipated and refuted Ellis's previously-recorded belief that 'inversion' was congenital, but Ellis still felt that R.'s inclinations might fit his Eonist paradigm, although he was careful not to play his hand too quickly, or too forcefully. In another letter to Haire, he confessed that 'R. is throwing up some fascinating challenges *[to his overall theory]* but may yet lead me to discover another sub-category of Eonist, rather than simply following the paths of Dr. Hirschfeld and co.'[16] With his customary gentleness, Ellis encouraged R. to talk about life after the end of the conflict. He was rewarded with far greater openness:

'Cliff's death made me feel that I should liberate myself as much as possible, because one never knows what's coming

16   Ellis to Haire, 28 March 1927.

next. But as soon as I found the courage to tell Marianne how I felt, she said that she had fallen in love with a young doctor – the kind of handsome, self-assured fellow I had come to envy more than anyone – and soon they were engaged. There were a few women with whom I had passing relations, usually people I met through my work as a medical secretary. They never lasted longer than a couple of nights, or a couple of weeks, but relations nonetheless. They would start with a friendly but conventional greeting, glances that lasted just a little too long, an awkward smile returned with an enthusiastic one, jubilant agreements to meet in the little coffee shop at the station, long walks and then furtive encounters at whoever's home was empty, and bitterly, we found that often, nobody's was … They fell apart for different reasons, greater than the lack of a room: we worried about what would happen if our families or friends found out, and our shared anxieties pushed us apart; they eventually realised that they were more interested in men and I saw, always too late, that even if they hadn't intended as such, their relationships with me had been merely a step towards working that out. I still longed for Marianne, even though I knew it was impossible, as I didn't even see her any more – I think she, or her family, knew how I felt about her, and kept her away from me. I struggled to sleep every night, broken, and fearful of how my loss would express itself in my nightmares.

'My parents wanted me to marry and have children – even more so after we lost Cliff. They tried to find me a suitor – another family friend's son, Gwyn, five years my senior, who had returned from the war, which had interrupted his Classics degree at Oxford. They introduced us over dinner, and I could see what was happening straight away – my mother had constantly been asking when I might meet a man and start a family. I could not find the heart to tell her the truth, so she kept pushing, and Gwyn was a frequent visitor, wanting to take me to balls, treat me to expensive meals and so on. I kept up the charade for months, trying to convince myself that I could love him, but I could not bear to let him touch me. After a couple of cold, fumbling attempts, I began to wonder if he too might have been an invert, but I never wanted to ask. We slept in separate beds whenever we had to spend the night together: it was my suggestion, but he never challenged it, and although we never raised it, I suspected that he felt the same way about things between us as I did: a kind, courteous friendship that was, at its heart, empty.

'At the same time, I began to think less about Marianne, and more of how I could change this situation, and yet how disappointed my parents would feel once they knew that I would not give them grandchildren. I met another woman, Clare, who had recently moved from London to Cardiff to work for the Independent Labour Party. She told me about balls in London where women could meet and dance together, how her friends would sometimes go to Paris or Berlin where it was easier to be honest about who they loved, and showed me some magazines that she kept hidden in her little apartment in Park Place. Clare made me forget about Marianne – she was beautiful in the same feminine way but more open with her emotions, helping me to express myself too. When Gwyn was away, she took me to London and we danced together. I borrowed a suit from Richard, a male invert that she knew. I felt and looked resplendent in traditional black tie, and that one night of waltzing with Clare in her beautiful ballgown, me taking the lead and then staying at Richard's house and strapping something to my waist so that I could make love to her. For both of us, it was heaven, for me because I'd never had the chance to be 'the man' with a woman before, and for her because she had never found anyone who had wanted to do that with her … We kept meeting whenever we could, asking each other if there was any way that we could make a life together, maybe in the Welsh countryside. Soon, the only time I would think about Gwyn was when Clare and I talked of how I might tell him and my family about what I really wanted to do, wondering how much easier it would be if I *were* Gwyn, and if a lady like Clare were taken with me … And that was when Gwyn proposed to me.

'From the way our conversation went, I immediately realised that I was wrong to think that Gwyn was an invert. I hesitated, and the look in his eyes betrayed him. I saw this desperation, a loneliness, because he had never met a woman who listened to him, who understood him, and over the time we'd spent together, I had come to see him as a very dear friend. I'd become his confidante, and maybe that was more important to him than anything else, but for me, that didn't mean love. As his face broke into a half-smile, I just said, 'I can't'. I tried to embrace him, hoping that he would realise that it wasn't *him*, but he ran out of the room, weeping. Immediately, my thoughts turned to my parents, and how I would explain.

'I didn't have to, though. When the subject came up, my mother said: 'It's Clare, isn't it?' I nodded, and she said, 'I knew it,' more in resignation than anger. 'I can't help it,' I told her. Then I went to see Clare, staying at her house for several days.'

As R. was obviously directing the exchange towards the idea – disavowed by both Hirschfeld and Ellis – that same-sex desire was inherently linked with cross-gender behaviour, Ellis suspected that R. had a background in sexology, or at least some working knowledge of it. In a letter to Haire, Ellis wondered if he would be better off talking to people with no prior interest in the field, who would bring no preconceptions to their meetings. He acknowledged, however, that he did not have the networks to facilitate this, and that relying on sexologists to provide his case studies was always likely to pose such a problem. He also confessed that 'R. is clinging, steadfastly, to my old idea of the 'invert', despite what I quite clearly see as identification with male objects of desire. The more I probe, the more R. asserts a sense of being psychologically and sexually masculine – drawn romantically towards women, and inclined towards masculine dress and behaviour – and I am wondering if I (and Dr. Hirschfeld, for that matter) have set up our excavations in the wrong place.'[17]

Haire's response was (characteristically) stern, telling Ellis that 'If you structure your enquiries around your anxieties about keeping up with the Germans, then your methodology will prove unsound. Respond to the person in front of you, who is surely complex enough to be interesting, regardless of your competitors, and re-evaluate your concepts accordingly. Enquiring into my dialogue with R. may be rewarding for you.'[18]

At Haire's suggestion, Ellis asked questions about R.'s acquaintance with Haire, and about how much R. knew of his own previous works, and of sexology and psychoanalysis in general:

'Once she had calmed down, my mother suggested I see a psychoanalyst. We found someone in Bristol, but I soon realised that this was not for me. *Everything* came back to my mother – his speculation about *her* being inverted, my desire to replace my father, or my brother, my jealousy of their anatomy, all that nonsense. After lots of time and money, my father said that I should meet his friend – Dr. Haire. After all, my father had a passing interest in sexology – he kept a few works in his library, and on my first visit, Dr. Haire lent me a copy of *Sexual Inversion* so I could read about other women like me.[19]

---

17   Ellis to Haire, 24 April 1927.
18   Haire to Ellis, 30 April 1927.
19   Note that Hirschfeld's *Transvestites* was not translated into English until 1991.

'I told Dr. Haire that I had always been drawn towards women – nervously, as the psychoanalyst had talked of perversion and pathology, and I had left his care worried about what might happen to me. Dr. Haire told me to relax – it was not illegal for women to love each other – but he understood that just because the law does not pay much attention to us, that does not always mean that society will be forgiving. Being open about it might cost me my family, my job, or my social standing, he said, and that would make life difficult even if I had support from Clare, and from her friends that I had met in London.

'I told Dr. Haire that I thought all this was especially cruel as I had never really felt like a woman. He asked what I meant, and I said that I had never liked doing all the things that women are supposed to do – wearing dresses, making the home, and so forth. 'Just because you don't feel drawn to 'the feminine' doesn't mean that you're not a woman', he said, asking me to elaborate. I told him about how Clare liked it when I penetrated her, and was happy for me to keep my hair short and go around in trousers, but that she wanted to be with a woman. Dressing in the manner I did – and *feeling* as I did – didn't mean that I wasn't a woman, she insisted. I wondered how much she loved me for my mind, especially as she never seemed too excited about the poetry that I wrote, and Dr. Haire told me to think more about my body. Was my discomfort with being a woman about my sex? *Did* I have 'penis envy'? If so, why? How long had I felt like this, beyond my youthful dressing-up?

'I couldn't separate that childish behaviour – which Dr. Haire said was very common in little girls, most of whom don't grow up to be inverts – from those dreams that I mentioned, my desire for Marianne, for Clare and those other women, or from my aversion to being seen or treated like a lady. I liked the magazines that Clare had shown me – certainly, I saw more of myself there than anywhere else, but still, I never felt like the women in their pages, no matter how I tried. I began to wonder: was I drawn to men after all? As well as women? At this point, Dr. Haire said that you were the best person in the country to talk to about all this, and promised to refer me.'

Ellis asked if wanting to be a man meant wanting to be the dominant partner in a lesbian relationship, and taking typically male social roles. R. said yes, but Ellis sensed that R.'s 'inversion' ran deeper than a desire to adopt masculine costume and mannerisms. In *Eonism*, Ellis specified 'two main types': 'the most common', in which 'inversion is mainly confined to the sphere of clothing', and the other, 'less common but more complete, in which ... the subject so identifies *[with]* the opposite sex that he feels really to belong to that sex', albeit with 'no delusion regarding his anatomical conformation'.[20] Ellis asked R. which type felt most appropriate. R. insisted: 'the second.' He then asked, 'would you like surgery to give you a male body?' R. replied 'yes'. It was a response that entangled Ellis's old and new ideas still further: for the first time, Ellis had met someone who had 'moved from psychological inversion towards *physical* inversion', but, he told Haire, he was 'still struggling for the terminology' to adequately differentiate between these desires.[21] His search for clarification would lead him into previously unchartered terrain – at least in his home country.

Ellis, Eonism and the demand for reassignment
More than seventy years old, Ellis now had to rethink his ideas about gender variance and sexual orientation,

---

20   Ibid., p36.
21   Ellis to Haire, 16 May 1927.

and how they related to each other, yet again. His 'two main types' of Eonist actually mapped closely to the 'transvestite'/'transsexual' distinction that would pre-occupy post-war sexologists, but his florid language lacked the clarity of his German counterparts, who were conducting sexological research and surgery in tandem, confirming the separation of gender and sexuality through praxis.

Having nothing like the same *milieu*, Ellis struggled with the thought that placing gender identity *above* sexual orientation would turn his categories upside-down: 'the invert would become heterosexual' after transition, he wrote to Haire, 'whilst the Eonist would be homosexual'.[22] Ellis had no framework for a bisexual (in the contemporary sense) person such as R. – who 'became quite excited' when Ellis mentioned the Institute for Sexual Science's surgical experiments, and decided that rather than try to untangle R.'s gender and sexuality through his Eonist theories, he would instead focus on R.'s gender identity issues, which seemed far more urgent. 'I tried to manage R.'s expectations, saying that such treatments were untested, physically dangerous and prohibitively expensive,' wrote Ellis, 'and, of course, these expectations, if realised, could consign all my exploration of Eonism to the past, but I feel I owe it to R., and doubtless many others – as well as *myself* – to explore the possibilities, and maybe see what might be feasible in the United Kingdom'.[23]

Ellis asked Haire – who was fluent in German – about Karl M. Baer (1885-1956), a German-Jewish author, suffragette and early Zionist, who became one of the first

---

22 Ellis to Haire, 12 July 1927.
23 Ibid.

people to undergo any kind of gender affirmation surgery, in December 1906, and was issued with a new birth certificate, legally confirming his gender.[24] Haire sent notes on Baer's book, *Aus eines Mannes Mädchenjahren*, a blend of autobiography and fiction, published under an obvious pseudonym, N. O. Body, in 1907 (translated as *Memoirs of a Man's Maiden Years* in 2005). Ellis also read about physicist, radiologist, and author Alan L. Hart (1890-1962), who had a hysterectomy and gonadectomy (ovary removal) at the University of Oregon Medical School in 1917-18, and then lived as a man, marrying a woman and setting up his own practice.

Wondering just how much he might be able to help R., Ellis inquired into work taking place under the auspices of Hirschfeld's Berlin-based *Institut für Sexualwissenschaft* (Institute for Sexual Science). He learned that in 1916, sexologist Max Marcuse had published a paper that distinguished desire for surgery from other forms of cross-identification, but Ellis's notes and letters do not mention the female-to-male 'transvestite' who apparently had his breasts and uterus removed in Berlin in 1912.[25] Haire gave him more information about Erwin Gohrbandt's (1890-1965) castration of Dörchen Richter in 1922, and told him the Institute was exploring vaginoplasty for male-to-female patients, drawing on 'transplantation' experiments that Austrian physiologist Eugen Steinach had done on rats and guinea pigs in the 1910s.[26] Ellis had written in 1913 that 'the characters in one sex must be latent in the

---

24 The exact details of the operations on Baer – who was most likely intersex – have never been found. Hirschfeld was a consultant, and it is possible that documents related to Baer were destroyed when the Nazis burned down the Institute for Sexual Science in 1933.

25 Meyerowitz, J. (2002) *How Sex Changed: A History of Transsexuality in the United States*. Cambridge/London: Harvard University Press, p18.

26 For a fuller discussion of Steinach, see Meyerowitz, pp16-17.

other', and it seems that the revelation that the Institute were leading in surgery (if not in endocrinology) stoked Ellis's friendly rivalry with Hirschfeld.

Whilst Ellis was conducting this research, Radclyffe Hall asked him to write an introduction to *The Well of Loneliness*. Hall described Ellis as 'the greatest living authority on the tragical problem of sexual inversion' and wanted her narrative authenticated as something that 'could itself stand as an inverted case history'.[27] Ellis obliged, and discussed Hall's manuscript with R. – a conversation that may have inspired him to say *The Well of Loneliness* presented, 'in a completely faithful and uncompromising form, one particular aspect of sexual life as it exists among us today' in response to the *Sunday Express'* campaign to ban the novel on its publication.[28] He spoke to R. about this in a new transcript, made on 19 August 1927:

'I saw more of myself in *[The Well of Loneliness]* than in any other story I've read. But I suppose the only thing that's even a little like it is *The Picture of Dorian Gray* and, well, it's not the same … I liked the way Stephen found out about inversion from reading her father's medical books … even if she had the chance to live in London and write novels in a way that I never did. I didn't think Stephen was happy to be in no-man's-land, and the ending make me cry[29] – I've never had the strongest of faiths but I've always felt like I was being tested, and I have talked to God so often, asking to be like the other girls at school, and then to be like the boys at Cliff's school, or the men at father's practice …'

27   Prosser. J. (1998) *Second Skins: The Body Narratives of Transsexuality*. New York/Chichester: Columbia University Press, p157.
28   http://spartacus-educational.com/Wradclyffe.htm, accessed 10 August 2018.
29   The novel concludes with Stephen's prayer: 'Give us also the right to our existence!' Hall, R. (1997) *The Well of Loneliness*. London: Virago, p447.

Ellis asked R. about the possibility of living as a man, taking a male name and wearing men's clothes, without surgical intervention. The latter would be expensive to obtain, most likely involving a trip to Germany for an experimental procedure.

'Of course, I have often thought about living like a man, as much as possible. I would call myself Robert and dress only in clothes from a tailor, like Stephen in *The Well of Loneliness*. But I would have to start again elsewhere. How would I tell my employer that I was coming back as a man? I know that it was more common before the war, but wouldn't it be strange now for them to have a male secretary? And then there are my parents – especially my mother. I think they would conclude that I was reacting to Cliff's death, trying to replace him somehow ... And then Clare ...'

Recalling R's statement that Clare wanted 'to be with a woman', Ellis asked if any relationship could be more important than feeling content in one's own body. (His handwritten annotations on the typed-up conversation include a frustrated note on his own 'impotence' and 'useless attraction to inverts' – most likely a reference to his marriage to the women's rights activist and open lesbian Edith Lees, which lasted from 1891 until Lees' death in 1916, despite the husband and wife not living in the same property.) R. said:

'Could I be happy in myself if I had to sacrifice the love of my life? Because I really fear that I would have to do so. I would have to find a completely different type of woman, who wasn't an invert but accepted that I had not always been a man. But if I *could* be completely male ...'

By now, Ellis was convinced that R.'s desires were sincere. They talked about the implications of R. acting upon them: the possibility of familial estrangement and being socially ostracised, as well as potential hardships in maintaining a relationship or employment. None of this was certain, Ellis insisted; people's reactions would be impossible to predict. Unlike a relationship, however, it would not be possible for R. to keep this transition secret from certain people, and so some difficult conversations became necessary. The toughest, they both knew, would be with R.'s parents. Aware that his presence would provide greater authority, R. asked Ellis if he could join them. Although he worried that this may break a boundary between the professional and personal that he had long struggled to maintain, Ellis agreed, and he sent a description of their meeting to Haire, which he kept in his case notes.

'I travelled to Cardiff to meet R.'s mother and father, who are ageing, but not entirely set in their ways – although I worried that they would react badly to R. bringing a sexologist, and might instead want R. to try again with a psychoanalyst. As a former doctor, at least, R.'s father seemed aware that we were discussing not so much a psychological ailment as a physical one, and that any treatment would be experimental – and possibly dangerous. As anticipated, it was R.'s mother who found it hardest to acknowledge R.'s decision. At first, her accusations were aimed at her long-standing and loving husband, not only for his prolonged absences during R.'s formative years, but also for his indifference towards R.'s youthful cross-dressing and masculine self-presentation in adulthood. R. tried to convince her that this was not her husband's fault, to little avail; instead, R.'s mother asked if Clare had 'led you astray', as it was 'only natural for *[Clare]* to wish there was a man' in their relationship. This hurt R. above all else, given how difficult this subject had been to broach, and I had to answer on R.'s behalf, insisting that R.'s bodily and romantic desires were not inherently linked.

'It was only when I insisted that R.'s desires were not as unusual as they might seem that R.'s mother broke down in tears of self-recrimination: bitter regrets about not raising R. to be more feminine, and that she was not able to persuade R. to marry Gwyn, who, she said, "would have supported you for life". In the silence that followed – just a moment, but one that felt like an age – she looked up and said, "Dear Lord, you have already taken my son ..." and, through her tears, "why are you taking my daughter as well?" She refused her husband's hand, and as R. rushed towards the bathroom, I knew I had to interject.

'I decided that first, I would assure her that other people had undergone such procedures and not just survived, but lived fuller, richer lives as a result. I praised R.'s bravery, and clarity of decision-making – nobody would undertake this, I said, unless they were completely certain in their decision. The cause might remain the subject of speculation, I continued, but that is for us, the sexologists. For everyone else in R.'s life, it would be best to offer support; "I appreciate that it might be daunting, but if you can find that in your heart," I told R.'s mother, "you will be rewarded with a level of love and kindness that you could never previously have imagined. There is nothing more I can add, but I wish you every happiness."'[30]

Ultimately, Ellis's intervention worked. He told Haire that while their relationship did not become as warm as they had hoped, R. avoided permanent estrangement from their family – partly because Ellis promised not to publish anything that would make them identifiable.

---

30   Ellis to Haire, 16 September 1927.

Having previously tried to manage his patient's hopes of getting surgery, Ellis spent more time exploring the possibility of achieving it in Britain, discussing the latest innovations in Germany in his letters with Haire.[31] The expertise that might have allowed this was not far off: South African-born surgeon Lennox Broster (1889-1965), based at Charing Cross Hospital, told Ellis that he had recently operated on a fifteen-year-old, raised as female, who had experienced virilisation – that is, deepening of the voice, clitoral enlargement and increased muscle strength.[32] Broster removed an enlarged adrenal gland but realised that its size was caused not by a tumour, but hyperplasia (an increase in organic tissue from cell proliferation). Broster continued his work on hyperplasia but also pioneered hormonal and surgical treatment to intersex patients – however, these breakthroughs were not made for nearly a decade. In 1936, Broster's operations on British women's champion javelin-thrower and shot-putter Mark Weston (1905-78), who was assigned female at birth, became global news. Weston was intersex; there is no evidence that Broster worked with transsexual people. However, Ellis's suggestion that R. meet Broster to discuss what might be possible only made matters more complicated, as the final transcript of R.'s testimony, dated 18 July 1928, makes clear:

'I made dinner for Clare and told her that I had something serious to tell her. She looked aghast: I think she thought I wanted to end things. So, I opened by saying, "I hope you can come with me …" and then I struggled to find the words. Finally, I managed to utter: "I've spoken to a surgeon …" And

31 Ellis to Haire, 3 October 1927.
32 Broster to Ellis, 23 October 1927.

I watched her eyes, expecting them to fill with tears, but she hadn't yet understood what I was saying, and I thought I should retreat. As I hesitated, she asked why.

'I said I couldn't keep lying to everyone. She still didn't know what I meant. "His name is Dr. Broster … He's looking at how to help women … who feel like … they should be … men." Now I saw a reaction: a strange mixture of anger, fear, and sadness, like she was staring at someone who had killed the woman she loved. In a sense, she was. "Can … can they even do that?" she asked. "Not yet," I said. "But they can make the body more comfortable." She asked what I meant. I said they could stop me bleeding, and give me a man's chest, if nothing else … And she said that she had never wanted to be with a man, not once. As I anticipated, she was giving me a clear choice.

'But what if I could be a man in public and a woman in private? It wasn't what I wanted, I said, but maybe there was a way of compromising, especially as Dr. Broster said that he didn't know if full surgery might be possible during my lifetime … But it was too late; those words had left my lips. Clare said she needed time to think, but I don't know why, I could see that her mind was already set. I went home, and wept, wondering what my parents would say; I did not see Clare for several days, and when I did, she told me that she no longer felt the same about me. Not just because of what I had said, but because I didn't discuss it with her before I saw Dr. Broster …'

With Ellis's help, R. planned for a new life. We know from another letter to Haire that R. continued to work as a medical secretary and saved up for a hysterectomy, gonadectomy and mastectomy,[33] but Ellis's notes and letters do not record any attempt to have phalloplasty. There was no suggestion that this would be possible any time soon: it was only after

33 Ellis to Haire, 4 September 1928.

the war that Michael Dillon became the first transsexual man to undergo such a procedure. Ellis's final notes record that R. had the planned surgeries at an unnamed hospital – most likely Charing Cross – and then moved to Rhyl, living as a man, finding work at a library and, as far as we can tell, no longer being involved with the sexological world.

By the end, Ellis felt that he had become far too entangled with R.'s personal life. He had gone well beyond the kind of detached observation and analysis that characterised his *Studies in the Psychology of Sex*, but told Haire that 'while I may have over-stepped the mark, both in my talk with R.'s parents and in my conviction that R. could help me to move past Dr. Hirschfeld's insights … I have few regrets about providing such assistance to R., and if time were not so pressing, I would readily do so again, although without investing so much hope of confirming my theory of 'Eonism', at least not for female Eonists'.[34] However, there is no mention in Ellis's archives of any serious attempt to return to the subject of gender variance in any papers relating to the final decade of his life. He might have become even more important to British trans history had he done so, but by this point, Grosskurth suggests, he realised that his youthful aim of solving the many problems of human sexual behaviour was beyond him and, realistically, beyond any lone individual.[35]

Perhaps, too, Ellis did not want the kind of attention that had come with *Sexual Inversion*. He was called as the star witness in the obscenity trial pursued against *The Well of Loneliness* in November 1928, around the same time as *Eonism* was published. Trying to avoid becoming too closely

---

34   Ellis to Haire, 18 September 1928.

35   Grosskurth, p. xv.

associated with the subject of homosexuality or 'gross indecency', Ellis pulled out of the Hall trial. Haire replaced Ellis in the witness box and argued (contrary to what R. had agreed with Ellis in private) that homosexuality *was* congenital, and that one could no more 'catch' it by reading books than one could contract syphilis in this manner.

A greater problem for Ellis, though, was that R.'s case stretched his Eonist categorisations past their limits. He needed to refine his second main type – those who felt they belonged to the 'opposite sex' – to include people who identified so strongly with that 'opposite sex' that they sought corrective surgery. In his semi-retirement, Ellis knew he would not be able to interview many people in order to formulate a theory of *why* they pursued this medical intervention, and rather than introduce this complication into *Eonism,* he merely acknowledged the five types of 'transvestite' identified in Hirschfeld's earlier work and then focused almost exclusively on male-to-female cross-dressers in his published text, without explicitly discussing surgery.[36]

Certainly, it is a shame that Ellis's previous assertion that the physiological characteristics of one sex were latent in the other – proved right by the surgeries that took place in the decades either side of his death – did not form the basis of *Eonism.* It is also regrettable that he was not able to further develop the idea that different gender expressions can be formed as much by social circumstances (be they within the family, or wider society) as by innate desires. Consequently, there was no school based on Ellis's ideas about gender identity, and the concept of 'Eonism' never gained significant currency. Hirschfeld's research into gender variance was

36 Ellis, Eonism, p10..

abruptly terminated in May 1933, when the Nazis attacked the Institute for Sexual Science and burned its library, and Hirschfeld died in exile two years later. Ellis lived until 1939, spending the last decade of his life writing about the idea of obscenity and, suffering from ill health, collecting his essays into volumes for posterity. Perhaps he intended to write separately about R., as suggested by the fact that he kept these notes on file, but there is no available evidence of him formulating them into a paper, let alone a new study on the psychology of sex. The questions that R. raised for Ellis were, tantalisingly, left unanswered.

CJ Ferguson (he/him) is a Ph.D. candidate and Associate Tutor in the Department of Gender Studies at the London School of Economics. His research focuses on female masculinity and the emergence of trans men during the inter-war period, and they were covered by mass media.

References

Ellis, Havelock. 1936. 'Eonism and Other Supplementary Studies' in *Studies in the Psychology of Sex, Vol. III, Part Two.* New York: Random House.

Grosskurth, Phyllis. 1980. *Havelock Ellis: A Biography.* London: Allen Lane.

Hall, Radclyffe. 1997. *The Well of Loneliness.* London: Virago.

Meyerowitz, Joanne. 2002. *How Sex Changed: A History of Transsexuality in the United States.* Cambridge/London: Harvard University Press.

Prosser, Jay. 1997. *Second Skins: The Body Narratives of Transsexuality.* New York/Chichester: Columbia University Press.

THE EXHIBITION

These letters, telegrams and newspaper cuttings were recently given to the Blackpool History Project, which tells the story of the town's entertainment industry. They were previously held by Blackpool Central Library: it is almost certain that Julian Cooper collected them, but it is unknown who originally donated them, or when, as Cooper had no direct descendants, and the Library kept no records. The report by Mass Observation – the organisation set up by Tom Harrisson, Humphrey Jennings and Charles Madge in 1937, using volunteer observers to record everyday life in the UK – has been reproduced from the archive at the University of Sussex, and provides further insight in Cooper's story. The Histroy Project is appealing for anyone with a copy of Cooper's book, long out of print, to come forward.

....

11 Long Acre, London, WC2.
Thursday, 2nd February, 1939.

Dear Mr. Cooper,

I regret to inform you that after an investigation into the missing £1 5s, as discussed with you and your colleagues last week, we have decided that we can no longer employ you as a chef at Hilton's. We have decided not to pursue the matter further, but ask that you do not contact anyone involved with the restaurant again.

Yours sincerely,

T. A. Hilton
Proprietor, Hilton's Restaurant, WC2.

*

LAID OFF BY HILTONS STOP UNABLE TO FIND ANY OTHER SOURCE OF INCOME STOP WILL THIS DEPRESSION EVER END STOP NO VACANCIES EVEN IN MILITARY STOP DESPERATE PLEASE STOP THE SILENCE YOUR DAUGHTER NEEDS YOU STOP

*

HAVE SOUGHT LEGAL ADVICE STOP INSIST YOU STOP

*

14, Three Colts Lane, London, E1.
Monday, 10th April, 1939.

Dear Mr. Hayward,

I heard about your House of Curiosities from a friend who visited Blackpool last summer, who was especially moved by the young hunger artist, and so I am writing to you with an unusual proposition, which I hope may be of interest. You may remember that I featured in the newspapers several years ago, after being charged with perjury and sent to H. M. Prison for Women at Holloway for marrying my sweetheart, Martha, under my alias of Julian Cooper. Imprisoned – not to mention bankrupted – by our 'justice' system, just for loving a woman enough to wed, and then disavowed by my family for good measure!

As you might imagine, life ever since has been rather challenging. I am constantly accused of masquerade, and I was released by my most recent employer after a journalist tracked me down and exposed

me to them. However, I believe that I can turn this situation into something mutually advantageous. My sex has long been the object of fascination for tittle-tattles, simpletons and the gutter press – why not make a show of it? I propose, simply, that I spend two months living at Blackpool beach on 'exhibition' for your visitors, allowing them to witness the person behind the lurid headlines. Please let me know if this sounds viable – I look forward to hearing from you soon.

Yours,

Mr. Julian Cooper, Esq.

*

> *14, Dene Road, Manchester, M20.*
> *Tuesday, 18th April, 1939.*

Dear Mr. Cooper,

Thank you for your recent letter, which, I must admit, intrigued me. Do you have an act, or are you proposing some sort of 'peep-show'? An exhibition of your domestic life would be considerably more appealing if you were to be with your 'sweetheart'. Would she be willing to participate? If so, we may be able to accommodate you both during our 'high season' of July and August, and could offer you a fee of twelve shillings per week for participating. If this suits, please let me know as soon as possible.

Yours sincerely,

Derek Hayward
Impresario, Hayward's House of Curiosities.

*

14, Three Colts Lane, London, E1.
Monday, 24th April, 1939.

Dear Mr. Hayward,

I am delighted that my suggestion has piqued your interest – it cannot have been typical of the proposals usually submitted to you. I am no longer with my 'sweetheart' – my court case, in which she denied knowledge of my birth sex, broke us apart – but I have discussed your ideas with my current beau, *Patricia. After a lengthy (and, I must concede, fractious) conversation, she has agreed to accompany me for the two-month period on the condition that she and I get an equal appearance fee, which we would like to know if you could raise to fifteen shillings, in light of our ongoing financial predicament. Patricia and I have been courting for two years and not yet had the opportunity to live together, so we would be happy to do so, even under such unorthodox circumstances. I look forward to making firmer arrangements in due course.*

Yours sincerely,

Mr. Julian Cooper, Esq.

*

14, Dene Road, Manchester, M20.
Thursday, 27th April, 1939.

Dear Mr. Cooper,

Thank you for your letter – I am, of course, perfectly happy to pay the same appearance fee to you and Patricia, but I am afraid

*that I cannot increase my offer of 12s, especially as I will also be
providing you with bed and board. This is the same as I paid to my
lion tamer before the tragic loss of his right arm, and to our famous
'Starving Brides' and their newly-wed husbands who fast for a
month to raise money to buy their first houses. It is even the same
as what I offered to the exiled Empress of Abyssinia to address the
crowds – it's up to you.*

Yours,

*Derek Hayward
Impresario, Hayward's House of Curiosities.*

*

Blackpool Observer, Tuesday, 27th June 1939.

Man-Woman Who Hoaxed the World to Masquerade at Blackpool Beach

By Graham W. Hawley

Julian Cooper, the woman who posed as a man in order to
join the army and become a husband, is to spend July and
August on the Golden Mile in Blackpool, living as a tourist
attraction over the busy summer season in an 'exhibition'
hosted by the ever-adventurous Derek Hayward at his
House of Curiosities. Visitors will be able to spend two
pence to see Cooper in one bed and her 'wife' in the other,
separated by a Belisha beacon but otherwise living as a
couple.

Cooper, who was born Millicent Hilda Warner-Cooper and was raised on a country estate near Reigate in Surrey, worked for the military as an ambulance driver (but was not, as she claimed, a Lieutenant) in Palestine after disguising herself as a man, but returned to London in 1927 and married a woman. Her true sex was only discovered once she went back to the Near East and was wounded at Hebron, whereupon she was sent for a routine medical examination. This eventually resulted in a perjury trial for marrying a woman with the assistance of a forged passport and birth certificate, and a six-month prison sentence – as well as public notoriety.

Cooper certainly makes a handsome (if conspicuously short) man, with a Brylcreemed side-parting and a sharp collection of suits. She is aware of the 'sex-change' solution taken by Mark Weston and Mark Woods, amongst others, who have recently undergone pioneering surgeries at London's Charing Cross Hospital, but is not interested in undertaking this drastic physical measure, and says she is 'not a hermaphrodite', or any other such medical curio.

'I wanted to join the army and see the world, so I gave my name as Julian in the hope of being able to defend my country', says Cooper, declining to explain why she felt the need to sustain her masquerade after being discharged. 'This desire led to me being disinherited and disowned, publicly humiliated and constantly unemployed. Did this happen to the men who came back from the Somme? Were they told they could only work if they did 'men's jobs' in the way that we were expected to do 'women's jobs'?' Since her first spell in prison, Cooper has worked as a cook, a puppeteer and been an amateur boxer, as well as returning to gaol in

1936 after being convicted for petty theft. However, she sees this summer 'on display' in Blackpool as a first step towards rebuilding her life.

'All the public know of me is what the newspapers have told them,' insists Cooper. 'Perhaps this exhibition will not give them the chance to get to know me, or to comprehend everything that has passed in my life, but it will allow them to empathise with my love and me – even here, we'll be kept apart. If nothing else, I hope that my stay will lead to greater understanding.'

In this unusual context, then, Cooper will finally get the chance to tell her own story, in the hope that it will find a more sympathetic audience than the judge and jury at the Old Bailey. As a resident of London, new to our town, Cooper may discover that the people of Blackpool are more compassionate, and more complex, than southerners often expect.

*

14, Three Colts Lane, London, E1.
Wednesday, 28th June, 1939.

My beloved Tricia,

I just read your letter, my heart growing heavier with every line.
I understand why you would not want to spend a summer living on Blackpool beach, with all the millers and weavers turning out to gawp at us. I don't *understand why you would think that I do. Do you imagine that, when I was growing up, it was my dream to debase myself before some two-bob impresario for the chance to exhibit myself alongside the Bearded Lady of Bridlington, or 'Charlie the Charleston Chicken'? To sit in a*

cabinet near a circus full of fleas that are too lazy to jump, and a hastily-stuffed whale called 'Moby Dick' – as if any of these people have ever read Melville? As Millicent, I could easily go back to Palestine – heaven knowns they always need ambulance drivers, whatever their sex – but I have remained in London, because I have always wanted to be with you.

You accuse me of being 'motivated entirely by money' – by what else should I be motivated? Can I pay my rent through charm alone? For ten years now, I have tried to make a living after becoming publicly known as the shameful 'Man-Woman', having 'journalists' find out where I work and force me out of the most menial jobs, and you begrudge me the only solution left?

I know it feels even worse than selling my story – like selling our story, minute-by-minute, day-by-day, week-by-week, for two months. I can only say that it will give me time to think, not just about who might publish such a story, but also about how I might make a viable living for both of us, for the foreseeable future. (Depending, of course, on what the Germans get up to, especially with their new friends in Spain.) I can only hope that this future will begin when I return from my summer holiday, once you have considered the lengths to which I have gone for you.

Yours, in love and sadness,

Julian.

*

14, Three Colts Lane, London, E1.

Wednesday, 28th June, 1939.

Dear Derek,

Unfortunately, Patricia has changed her mind about appearing with me. Any chance you could find me a new 'wife'?

Yours hopefully,

Julian.

*

14, Dene Road, Manchester, M20.
Friday, 30th June, 1939

Dear Julian,

Please don't fret – I have arranged someone for you. She is an experienced performer, having been working as a clairvoyant for several years, and moon-lighting as a bearded lady. (She picked up the Yorkshire accent surprisingly quickly, for someone from Kiev.) I will introduce you on your arrival on Sunday, I feel confident that you will excite each other – and the punters.

Yours,

Derek.

*

The Promenade, Blackpool, FY1.

Sunday, 2nd July, 1939.

Tricia,

I met my new 'wife' yesterday. And – I hate to say it to you, but – she was an absolute hoot!

She started off by reading my palm, in this thick Russian accent. (I asked her about that later – her family were Whites, she said, who fled the Bolshevik tyranny. I explained about some of my tear-ups with the Reds, and she thanked me for helping to stop them ruining our country like they've ruined hers.) I have 'fire hands', she told me, with a long palm and short fingers, which causes me to love and hate with intensity, take risks and believe in myself, no matter what this world puts in my path. (I'm certain that you will recognise this portrait, dear!) The Mount of Mercury, just below my little finger, gives me a 'sharp sense of humour' and helps me to adapt to any situation – which may prove as useful on Blackpool beach as it was at Her Majesty's Pleasure.

She told me that 'your life-line is deep', saying that this didn't necessarily mean getting into old age as much as being 'full of élan vitale'. (That's 'life-force' to you and me.) However, she said, the 'line of destiny' down the middle of my palm means that my life will be moulded by factors beyond my control, and that I had to do everything in my power to take charge of my own fate. I couldn't decide if being drawn to wear trousers was beyond my control or not, but by asserting myself as Julian, I realised, I could take charge of myself, and create for that self a whole new destiny.

Then we both fell over laughing …

Yearning for you, darling – I'll be living with Petya, but thinking of you …

Dreaming of the future, from the Mount of Mercury – Julian.

*

Blackpool Observer, Thursday, 6th July, 1939.

'MAN-WOMAN' EXHIBITION FAILS
TO KEEP PUBLIC GUESSING

BY GRAHAM W. HAWLEY

The newest resident at Hayward's House of Curiosities is their least exciting yet. Perhaps, that is the point. After a decade in and out of the headlines, and the Holloway Prison for Women in London, it is understandable that Lt. Julian Cooper – formerly posted to Palestine with the British Army, and born Millicent Hilda Warner-Cooper – would desire a quiet life. Why, then, live that life on Central Beach, in a manner more akin to the elephants at London Zoo than those brave men, and women, who risked everything at the Western Front before settling back into the society that they saved?

Cooper may not *like* the limelight – or, in this case, beacon-light – but seems unable to stay out of it. A poster on the side of the building where Cooper and her 'wife' Petya will live for the next two months, behind a glass wall for which people have to pay tuppence for the privilege of seeing through, says 'HOW LONG CAN A LOVING COUPLE REMAIN UNDER THESE CONDITIONS?' A more urgent question, especially for impresario Derek Hayward, might be – how long can the public stick around without getting bored?

I queued for an hour, and then stayed for ten minutes, witnessing the 'dramatic steps' that Cooper has taken 'for the woman I love', which on this occasion was to read *The Daily Mail* whilst her 'wife', a Russian fortune-teller named Petya whom Cooper apparently wooed whilst on holiday in Skegness three years ago, smoked a cigarette. They looked like they had never met – the light pecks on the cheek, all that common decency allows, were unconvincing, and the utterly cautious way they moved around each other, and the Belisha beacon that separated their two beds, did not give the impression of two people who knew each other intimately. The beacon is 'a symbol of futuristic love', according to Mr. Hayward, but if this is the future, then he can keep it. While the 'Man-Woman' Cooper didn't look like your average Lieutenant, the kisses wouldn't have looked out of sorts in any Hollywood film, even the ones made since the restrictive Motion Picture Production Code was introduced a few years ago. In all my years covering the holiday season here, I have seen defrocked priests share cages with lions, women risk their lives on the trapeze, and even a bearded lady perform with more zest and enthusiasm than these two. Unless Mr. Hayward, and Mrs. and Mrs. Cooper, can find some 'dramatic steps' to take, then the crowds here are going to fall away in haste.

*

The Promenade, Blackpool, FY1.
Friday, 7th July, 1939.

My dearest Tricia,

I don't know if the papers in London are carrying any news from the 'Golden Mile', but somehow, I rather doubt it. (I am reading the nationals here and they are far more concerned with Mr. Hitler, who doesn't seem sure if he wants to be content with Czechoslovakia, build up the Spanish or jump into bed with the Reds, or at least that's how they tell it.) Just in case some awful rag like the City and East London Observer *considers one of their (adopted) locals taking a sea-side holiday to be worth their time, I wanted to make sure that you, if not the wider public, hear my truth before their lies.*

The little pimp who interviewed me for the Blackpool paper last week, one Graham Hawley, has decided that he considers our show perverse – and worse, dreadfully dreary. How tiresome are these people who cannot even admit their own titillation! His hit-job has spooked Derek, who is now demanding Petya and I 'liven things up a bit.' He was livid that Hawley said it looked like Petya and I had never met – a bloody cheek given that we'd just spent an hour over tea – and insisted it 'won't stand' that we had tourists whistling to try to get a rise out of us, waving bank-notes at us, pulling stupid faces like children, standing in front of us eating, etc. So, now, Derek is bursting into our cage – let's face it, that's what it is – and insisting that we 'show a little more affection', adding 'if you catch my drift' and then a wink, because Petya and I really are *that stupid. So far, we have just had a little canoodling, which has got the crowds talking – how dull their lives must be! – and which should be enough to keep the puppet-master off our backs for now. But please, take it from me, my love for you is undimmed, and I really wish that* you *were here – then we could really liven things up ...*

Yours, always,

Julian.

*

*Mass Observation report from the
Golden Mile, Blackpool, Friday, 14th July, 1939.*

Holiday-makers pass in a near-continuous line, sometimes queuing at peak periods, although the exhibition has not been as popular as its proprietor had hoped. People stare down into the box containing Lt. Cooper and his/her bride, kept moving by attendants. Stream of remarks:

A LAD SAYS [*directed at Cooper*]: You silly old bugger!
ATTENDANT: Pass no remarks, please.
MAN: You're a disgrace to this country!
ATTENDANT: Again – no remarks.
THE MAN: He never were a lieutenant.
ATTENDANT: I don't care if he were a private.
WOMAN: He looks very much like a he, doesn't he?
WOMAN: He doesn't *do* much, though. Doesn't a military man like him miss the action?
MAN: What's to stop him crossing over to his wife's bed?
ATTENDANT: Nothing much, except he'll lose the wager.
WOMAN: How much did he bet?
ATTENDANT: £250.
MAN: [Whistles]
WOMAN: Do you want to stay and see if he wins?
MAN: How long do we give it? I can't hang about all summer.
A LAD: What if he has a nightmare and starts sleep-walking?
ATTENDANT: They're watched all the time. If one gets up, the other has to stay in bed.

WOMAN: Has he had one of those operations?

ATTENDANT: I can't tell you that.

(Disappointed noises amongst the crowd.)

MAN: It all sounds rather dull.

WOMAN: They certainly look bored. *[Directed at Cooper]* Liven up, ladies!

A LAD: Can't you tell 'em to make it more exciting?

MAN: What can be done if they're not allowed to touch each other?

WOMAN: I'd be boring for two hundred and fifty quid.

MAN: You can do that for free, love!

WOMAN: Ooh, the bloody cheek!

HER FRIEND: I like how quiet it is. Gives me time to think, too.

HUSBAND: You can think at home, darling. I don't save up all year to watch people sitting around doing nothing.

WOMAN: You can see the love in their eyes, though – look at how they're looking at each other!

The attendant prattles on. 'Lt. Cooper is on the left. Keep moving please. He's three weeks down there and has another five to go. For those of you jeering and demanding more for your tuppence, I ask you to think about how hard it is to do nothing for so long, especially when so consumed by the love of your life.' The crowd continued to file past, bored, and it is hard to imagine what Cooper, his/her bride or the impresario might do to shake things up.

*

CHURCH GROUPS PROTEST AGAINST 'JULIAN COOPER'
EXHIBITION ON GOLDEN MILE

BY GRAHAM W. HAWLEY

Yesterday, Lt. Julian Cooper's 'exhibition' on the Golden
Mile took its strangest turn yet, as a group from the parish
church of Blackpool St. John the Evangelist turned up to
protest against what they called the 'base immorality' of
the show. The crowd of twenty found themselves in an
unexpected alliance, as they were led by Simon Garrett –
whose wife, 'Petya', legally known as Laura Sampson-Jones,
has been masquerading as Cooper's partner, and getting
rather closer to 'Julian', legally known as Millicent Hilda
Warner-Cooper, than he might have liked. It has transpired
that Sampson-Jones, who normally makes her living as a
fortune-teller in Skegness during the summer months whilst
working as a weaver for the rest of the year, had misled her
husband about the nature of her employment in Blackpool,
and word had reached him, leading him to spear-head this
most unorthodox protest.

The group turned up outside Cooper's box around 10
a.m., holding hand-made placards bearing slogans such as
'Don't Go Against God', or Deuteronomy 22:5, declaring
that, *'A man's item shall not be on a woman, and a man shall
not wear a woman's garment; whoever does such a thing is an
abhorrence unto Adonai.'* Garrett stood in front of the box,
his back to the courting couple, telling the audience how
impresario Derek Hayward had all but forced his wife into

this sham 'marriage' being played out on Blackpool beach.

Hayward's attempts to get the protesters to move on were unsuccessful. Initially, he quietly asked them to leave as they were 'scaring the punters', but Garrett pointed out, to considerable laughter, that the demonstration had attracted the largest crowd to the display since its opening. Hayward's threat that he would call the police generated further mirth, as someone told him that they were more likely to arrest the facilitator of 'such depravity' than those trying to keep it out of the public eye. Perhaps the audience might have been persuaded to disperse if the lion who, two summers ago, mauled its 'tamer', had still been present, but as it was, Miss Cooper and Mrs. Sampson-Jones posed little threat, banging on their cage to jeers before hiding in their separate beds in a tedious counter-protest against the self-appointed moral guardians. It may well prove to be the most exciting moment of their exhibition, which is scheduled to last for another six, long weeks.

*

The Promenade, Blackpool, FY1.
Friday, 21ˢᵗ July, 1939.

Dear Tricia,

Do you miss me? Your letters are yet to reach me, although I'm sure that you're sending them, around your busy life in London.

That Hawley fellow is still printing the most despicable things about me in what passes for the local newspaper, and I have good mind to complain to their editor, although I suspect he has put Hawley up to all this. So, screw Hawley – I think his hostility emboldened a Christian group to protest against us earlier this week. Amidst all the shrieking about sin and vice, I learned that the reason why 'Petya' had such mastery of the Yorkshire accent is because she's from York, and working in Skegness over the summers did not change it much – and, of course, her 'Russian exile' persona was a sham!

How could I have been so stupid as to be taken in by such an obvious falsehood? As if anyone makes a living here by being themselves! I feel such an idiot – it's not as if I actually believed all that clap-trap about the line of destiny or the mount of Mercury, so how did I fall for that phoney accent? Why didn't I ask her any more questions about her apparent time in Kiev, or her family's brave escape from the Bolshevik hordes? I had three weeks in a cage with her, after all – so much for not enquiring out of 'politeness'!

I confronted her about all this, waiting until sundown so that all the crowds – such as they were – had moved on. I worked myself into a lather, listing everything she had lied to me about, having stewed over it for several hours as we silently shifted around our little box. As soon as I launched into my tirade, she – Petya – LAURA – just laughed in my face. Of course she did! I couldn't stop myself: I raised my hand and, when she suddenly became serious, I shoved her. Fortunately, she just fell onto the bed, got up and told me that she was leaving, and that she would tell Derek everything that had happened. As always, it seems, I was the monster ...

I spent the night alone, thinking more of you than anyone or anything else, trying to ignore that stupid beacon and its flashing red light. Just as I finally managed to get a few winks, in burst Derek, insisting that unless I accepted a new 'wife', he'd throw me out.

This was rude enough – but before I could admonish him about 'Petya', he told me that he'd tracked down Martha – a decade since I last heard from her – and that he would ask her to be my wife, just like I did after our magical weekend on the Brighton sea front all those years ago! I told him that she would certainly decline, and asked him how he'd found her; all he would say was that her name had been in the papers, and that he was well-connected. (I thought that someone so resourceful and influential would probably have got more out of life than running a two-bit human zoo in the tawdriest bit of Blackpool, but I refrained from saying so – perhaps for the best.) By this time, the first holiday-makers had drifted by in search of a little distraction from their dismal lives, and they stopped to watch Derek and I have a fearsome argument, as he screamed about how much I had cost him, insisting that I was on my 'final warning'.

Once he calmed down, I suggested that the only way to save the show was to bring in my real wife – this might introduce some genuine spark into things, provide some more publicity and make me (and, by extension, the audience) happy and most of all, make sure that he keeps us in bed and board for another month whilst we work out what to do next. Would you be willing to reconsider and spend a few weeks by the sea with me? I understand that it's not the most enticing offer I have ever made to you, but it might be the most urgent.

Yours in love and, let's be honest, desperation,

Julian.

*

37 Coburn Street, London, E3.
Monday, 24th July, 1939.

My darling Julian,

Of course I miss you! I have received your letters, and written several times to your address on The Promenade – I don't understand why they aren't reaching you. (They don't have anyone using them as food to tame a lion, do they?)

I have given notice at the office and will come to be with you tomorrow afternoon. Tell Derek, or his representative, to meet me at Blackpool North Station at five o'clock.

Yours, until soon,

Tricia.

*

Blackpool Observer, Thursday, 3rd August, 1939.

JULIAN COOPER 'EXHIBITION' DESCENDS FURTHER INTO FARCE AS 'REAL' WIFE STAYS FOR JUST ONE WEEK

BY GRAHAM W. HAWLEY

The saga of 'Lt. Julian Cooper' and Derek Hayward's Golden Mile 'exhibition' collapsed from tragedy into farce yesterday, as Cooper's 'real wife', introduced to their dwindling public only as 'Patricia', walked out after just one week.

Finding that the incorporation of Cooper's 'childhood sweetheart' did nothing to draw people back to the 'freak-show' on the sea-front, and aware of the difficulties of winning back their audience after Cooper's previous accomplice, Laura Sampson-Jones, was exposed as a fraud, Hayward set the couple a number of challenges, intended to liven up the show. In addition to maintaining the established rule that the lovers were not allowed to enter the same bed, these included: writing love poetry to each other, which the attendants would then read to the crowd; learning how to juggle or ride a unicycle, within the tiny space; and fasting for twenty-four hours or more, during which they would be tempted with fruit, cakes and little sandwiches.

After the crowd implored her for twenty minutes to start juggling, with jeering chants of 'clown!', 'Patricia' (if that is her real name) lost patience, and stormed out of the box – Mr. Hayward later said that she had returned to her hotel, checked out and boarded the first train back to London, without stopping for her appearance fee. What this means for her relationship with Cooper, if indeed they *are* an item, remains to be seen: such court-ship is not outlawed, despite Conservative M.P. Frederick MacQuiesten's effort to extend the 'gross indecency' clause of the Criminal Law Amendment Act to women in 1921, but the weight of disapproval will doubtless be even heavier after Cooper dragged 'Patricia' into her public notoriety.

That notoriety, however, will no longer shame or bore Blackpool, as Mr. Hayward declared this to be the final straw, and closed Cooper's exhibition one month ahead of schedule, to little discernible reaction. It is understood that Cooper has also returned to London, without leaving any contact details. It is not yet confirmed if Mr. Hayward will find anyone else to live in his famed House of Curiosities for the next month, especially given the current political situation, but even left unoccupied, Cooper's box could hardly prove less stimulating.

*

Picture Post, Saturday, 23rd April, 1955.

LT. JULIAN COOPER'S OWN STORY
NOTORIOUS 'MAN-WOMAN' BREAKS HER SILENCE

BY ROBERT PARKER

More than twenty years since being sent to prison for perjury for marrying a woman, and more than a decade since her infamous 'exhibition' at Blackpool beach, Lt. Julian Cooper has spoken for the first time about her extraordinary life, as she prepares to publish a sensational memoir.

'Everything I want to say about that man Hayward and his loathsome 'House of Curiosities' is in my book', says Cooper, 'and I don't want to waste any more time on him, except to say that he was the only person ever to make me side with the Inland Revenue, and I am delighted they closed down his tawdry freak-show. I am happy, also, that I walked out, and was able to go straight into a job with the Army, driving an ambulance, before I was discharged and went into the Home Guard, where I was treated with dignity.'

Astonishingly, given all of her prior tribulations, Cooper served her country throughout the Second World War as a man, insisting that her sex was never questioned – the headlines that blighted her throughout the Thirties never came back to haunt her. 'We were fighting Hitler,' snaps Cooper. 'Why would anyone care about what was on my birth certificate?' Drawing on a cigar, she continues, 'I never wanted to have any operations or anything like that. I wanted to serve my country before all the hoo-ha in the newspapers, and despite everything, I still wanted to afterwards, and so I did – I felt, in 1939 as I did in 1917, that the best way to make a career in the military would be to do so as a man. The Home Guard didn't accept women in this war any more than the Royal Fusiliers did in the last one.'

Why, then, live as a man for her entire adult life – including that ill-fated stay on Blackpool beach? 'If I couldn't convince a court of why I did it, when my life practically depended upon my doing so, how on Earth could I explain it to you? The truth is, I could never sincerely explain it to myself. In some ways, it felt comfortable – natural, even. I cannot express it in any more depth than that. All I can say is it was the only way for me to marry the woman I loved, or to go back into the military – the only place that ever felt like home. I was never able to persuade my family of my reasons, any more than I could anyone else, and they cut me off entirely after I was sent to prison – my parents refused my attempts to contact them until they both died, during the war. My inheritance went to every other member of the family, and I never went back to the farmhouse where I grew up.'

Does this mean, then, that Cooper is hoping to capitalise on the fame earned by another former soldier, the American GI turned 'blonde beauty' Christine Jorgensen or, closer to home, the racing driver-turned-woman Roberta Cowell? 'I'm not like them,' insists Cooper, reminding me that she had contemporaries who *did* undergo surgery to turn them into men, but chose not to investigate such possibilities herself. 'At last, I'm happy with who I am, and with the woman I love. I just want to talk about what happened to me as a result of attempting to live truthfully to myself, and to make life a little easier for those who follow my lead – I'm trying to be as optimistic as I can about that, but now my book is finished, why should I care anymore?'

Lt. Julian Cooper's memoir, An Imperfect Gentleman, *is published by Neptune Books in May.*

DANCING WITH THE DEVIL

Laura Miller was born in Coventry in 1927. This extract from Dancing with the Devil *picks up her story on her return to the UK after three years in New York, where she worked as a cabaret performer, dancer, and waitress at the infamous Club 82, operated by the mafia when gay bars and female impersonation were illegal. She moved to London in 1955, and eventually began a new career as a model. After the events outlined below, she withdrew from public life; little has been heard from her since she published this memoir in 1970.*

....

Click, click, click. I'd become used to the cameras, and in a way, I liked the fact that none of the photographers gave a sailor's cuss about me beyond how I looked. I'd had enough of telling people who I was, what I thought and how I felt, only for them to turn around and insist that I was wrong. Now – once I'd gone through the daily rigmarole of making myself look presentable – my exchanges were simple. I made the face they wanted; they captured it on film. Occasionally, I had to remind myself not to blink on the flash, but that was as hard as it got. *Click, click, click.*

I knew it *could* become harder at any moment. Someone just had to go to the press. My brother could be rat enough, I often thought, snitching on me to the papers like he always did to my parents. By this point, though, I figured that if he hadn't done it, he probably wouldn't. If he was waiting for my stock to rise further, he was in for a disappointment – the public might not have known my secret, but the industry did. I'd auditioned enough of Britain's actors, so to speak, for word to get around, and I couldn't help wondering if that was the reason why other people moved rapidly from non-speaking extra parts to speaking ones to supporting roles when I was never allowed a word on film. (After I'd done all that work on my voice, too.) The Wolfenden Report hadn't landed yet, and if those actors were wondering about whether sleeping with me made them a 'pansy', then they were probably worried that it could land them in jail. Perhaps only a few of them boasted about a night in my bed, then, but how could I know? Something was holding me back, and it seemed more likely that than anything else.

I noticed more than one of my conquistadors bravely avoiding my glance at the *Dance with the Devil* wrap party. One man, though, caught my eye. At first, he looked just like any other suit at these things – the main difference was the way he looked at *me*, a casual smile that said he was more curious about my soul than my sex. His only distinguishing feature was that he was shorter than all the men and most of the women (not that there were many) and a good six inches shorter than me. It looked like he'd come alone, and he was one of the few people who didn't seem unable or unwilling to approach me. As soon as he said 'hello, I'm Frank,' I knew something was up. He sounded like his voice never broke, and for a split second, I envied him more than I'd ever envied anyone, before I thought what a nightmare that must have been during his schooldays. Anyhow, he wasn't unattractive, smooth skin and slick hair, like a softer Cary Grant, so I held my tongue. Then I wondered: *Did he* know *about me? Is he* like *me?*

We got talking, and he told me he was setting up a London office for his father's tea business because his family were thinking of leaving India since independence and the partition, because of what he described as 'Nehru's creeping Bolshevism'. He had a calm, gentle manner that put me at ease, and was quite upfront when I asked what brought him to the party. His family were 'philanthropists', he said, passionate about culture, often putting money into 'high-brow' films like this one. Then, he became more interested in me, asking questions that might seem obvious, but hardly any man ever cared to pose. How did I get into the film industry, or modelling? Given how charming and beautifully spoken I apparently was, why wasn't I better known? Did I want to be? What were my hopes, ambitions, and dreams?

We chatted all evening, helped by the copious free booze – all that champagne, I joked, made me feel like Princess Margaret. Frank laughed, and if what he'd already told me didn't make it clear why my remark made him a bit self-conscious, what I saw next did. When the party ended, I offered to take him to my bedsit in Soho, figuring that we'd have more fun than I did on my quiet nights in with fumbling, awkward men. Politely, he suggested his place might be a bit more comfortable, and I wasn't going to argue. It's incredible, really, how near Soho is to Mayfair, and yet …

After a short taxi ride (which he covered, aware that being an occasional model and even more occasional film extra wasn't even as glamorous as it looked) we reached the penthouse flat that was the Bolton-Taylor Company's main London residence. First, he showed me the roof terrace, pointing out Marble Arch and Hyde Park, saying we couldn't see Buckingham Palace from here but talking about 'Queen Liz' with such affection that I wondered if they were friends. Then he apologised for the mess inside the apartment, as if mine didn't resemble the aftermath of the Blitz. He had contracts and letters, Liberal pamphlets and film magazines, suits in the wardrobe and underwear on the floor, mainly gents' but a few ladies', which made me wonder if I was going to become his mistress.

After a long chat and plenty more to drink, he took my hand, stroking it. He ran the tips of his fingers up to mine, noticing the polish and running his thumb over my index fingernail. He looked at me and smiled; sensing his hesitation, I took a chance and drew him to my lips. Suddenly liberated, he started kissing me, and I genuinely thought – hoped – that he would never stop. Then he stroked his hand down my face and onto my neck, gently caressing it until he noticed my Adam's apple.

'*I thought you knew,*' I said.

'I thought *you* knew,' he replied with a strange half-smile.

'Knew what?'

He stood, unbuttoned his shirt and took off his belt.

'I don't know what the word for it is, but I'm seeing a doctor on Harley Street ...' He let his trousers drop. 'If only we could have swapped bodies, eh?'

I put my arm around his shoulders and kissed him. I think we both knew that there were many more revelations to come. But they could wait.

*

After *Dance with the Devil,* a director offered me a small speaking role. I was only going to be in one scene, and the film didn't look amazing – a screwball comedy called *All Over the Shop,* about a maverick greengrocer – but it was a big step up from walking on, shooting a sultry glance at the man behind the camera and walking off again. *Maybe you should get an agent,* Frank joked at a celebratory meal (which, once again, was his treat). Then there was a pregnant pause.

'You arranged this?' He looked at me, knowingly. 'Oh, darling,' I said, 'you didn't have to do that.'

'I didn't go out of my way – just put in a word for you over dinner. The casting agent is friends with my brother.'

'I thought your family only got involved with "high-brow" films,' I replied.

'You'll make it classier,' he insisted, and raised his glass.

The rest of the night was a bit of a blur. But as I woke up in Mayfair – and in Frank's arms – the next morning, I thought about how I'd finally landed on my feet. No more waiting on boorish Americans who wanted me on the side but blew their tops if I ever dared suggest being anything more. No more dancing for punters who cheered and leered when I was on stage but treated me like dirt when I was off it. No more competing with the girls to be these mobsters' favourites when we should have been looking after each other; and, best of all, no more worries about the New York mafia's protection racket, and no more feeling like I'd be cast out into the street if I didn't give in to their every whim. Now, I had Frank. I know every woman says her man is *different,* but mine really was.

Clearly, even this fleeting moment of happiness, attached to a handful of lines in a stupid farce, meant I was getting too far out of my box. I was back in Soho, trying to make my hovel look like a home, or at least inhabitable, when I got a phone call.

'Laura, it's me.' Frank sounded flustered – not his usual self. 'They're onto us.'

'Wait, hold on,' I replied. 'Who's "they"?'

'The *Daily Chronicle*.'

'Oh, Christ. Who told *them*?'

'I don't know.'

'How did you hear about it?' I asked, momentarily worried that I'd been wrong about Frank, and that like everyone else, he didn't have my interests at heart after all.

'My brother just called me,' Frank said. 'He used to be a journalist.'

'He told them?'

'No!' said Frank. 'He mentioned you to a friend, who'd heard about it, and tipped him off.'

'Does this friend know who the reporter is?'

'No, he tried to find out, but no-one would tell him.'

'Jesus wept … Any idea what they're planning?'

'No,' Frank replied. 'I think they've just heard a rumour for now. Have you noticed anyone or anything strange around you lately?' I hesitated. 'Apart from me, of course,' he laughed.

His joke snapped me out of a dark train of thought. If we were both going to be exposed, then I could lose all my film work, probably my modelling as well, and I didn't fancy the idea of spending my life in the papers or on the television letting the vultures pick at my guts like Christine Jorgensen – if anyone would even listen. At best, it would be back to Club 82 and the mob; at worst, the game. Somewhere between the two laid the end of Blackpool pier. None of them appealed. As for Frank – he had the emotional support of his family, though they weren't exactly thrilled about the whole thing, but he worried they'd take his name off the business, which could mean losing his income entirely. However this might pan out, it didn't look good.

My next thought was to wonder who might have sold us out, and whether I would go to the trouble of stringing him up from the nearest lamp-post or simply wring his neck. Perhaps it was one of the furtive blokes at the wrap party, or maybe the *Chronicle* had sent some private dick along to that because they *already* knew and wanted to find out more; seeing that I was trying to form a relationship for them to destroy was an added bonus. (And people said the way *I* lived was disgusting.)

'If you can't beat them, join them,' said Frank over an expensive consolatory dinner.

'How can we *join* them?' I asked.

'They've been snooping on you, right? Following you around, trying to find people who know you, going through your bins?'

I didn't *know* if anyone had done this, but I'd put nothing past these people, so I just nodded.

'Two can play *that* game,' said Frank. 'I'm going to hire someone. A private investigator that our firm have used. Mate's rates. He knows about me and he's fine with it, so he won't have any problems with you.' He paused, smiling as I raised an apprehensive eyebrow. 'Mad as it sounds, some of these detectives are actually decent chaps.'

'What good will it do?'

'Well – we find out who this reporter is and what he's got. Then we can work out how to stop him. First, we'll try to reason with him. Unlikely – so if that doesn't work, and he's not scared off by the fact that unlike most of the people they go for, we can actually answer back, then we threaten to take him to court.'

'Won't they have better lawyers?'

'Maybe, but do they really need this story that much? It's not like we're Prince Rainier and Grace Kelly or anything.'

'No, I suppose not.'

I thought for a moment. Perhaps I looked slightly peeved (justifiably in my opinion, if not his) at Frank suggesting I wasn't as important as Princess Grace of Monaco. He looked into my eyes, smiled and took my hand.

'What if they won't budge?' I asked him. 'Would we still be able to sell them my story as an exclusive? That'd give me a bit of control, at least.'

'And risk all your work?'

'It might be all right,' I replied. 'And it sounds like it's going to happen anyway.'

'I think we can stop it,' Frank insisted. 'It's worth a pop.'

Frank's mate was called Derek – an affable fellow who played rugby, went to the opera, and listened to the BBC Third Programme. He was worlds apart from the boys I grew up with in Coventry, or the girls I danced with in New York. I ended up spending a *lot* of time with him, as he constantly had to be at my side to look out for anyone shifty enough to be a reporter. It seemed pointless: they had their story, and it was just a matter of time before they confirmed it. However much he looked after me, promising that I could stay at his place if I couldn't meet the rent on my shabby bedsit and telling his film contacts to keep looking for work for me, I couldn't help thinking that Frank was more worried about his reputation than mine, and I thought that the best outcome now might be a preposterous tabloid exposé of my 'red-hot affair' with a private detective (who, really, was one of the most sexless people I'd ever met).

So, there I was, going everywhere with this man who was trying not to be seen with me, in a hunt for another man who was trying not to be seen looking for me. Meanwhile, Frank and I kept going out on the town, a masked ball here, a private member's club there, avoiding the film world (apart from the shoots for *All Over the Shop* – which, it was becoming apparent, was not going to be on the level of *Kind Hearts and Coronets*, limiting its ambitions to ripping off Norman Wisdom's *Trouble in Store*) because it was the obvious place to find us. After a long night that began in a theatre (to see if all the fuss about *The Mousetrap* was warranted) and ended in a taxi from a dance hall in Chelsea, where I taught him how to take the lead in the Charleston, we got back to Frank's flat to find a sealed envelope, with no name, in his letterbox. He opened it right away.

'I'VE SEEN YOUR MAN IN THE SHADOWS, TRYING TO KILL OUR STORY – YOU SHOULD TELL HIM TO GET A LESS JAZZY CAR. FIFTY POUNDS WILL KEEP YOUR NAME OUT OF THE PAPERS. MEET ME IN SOHO ON TUESDAY AT 10 P.M. – LOCATION T.B.C.'

'Well, at least we know why Derek was so cheap,' I sighed, as I watched Frank's hands tremble. 'Should we go to the police?'

'Who knows what they'll do?' Frank replied. 'They might even be in on it. Even if they're not – do you think they're going to side with the likes of us?'

'I don't expect much, but when it's this clear-cut …'

'They wouldn't be so clear-cut if they didn't think they'd get away with it,' said Frank.

'You're not going to pay them?'

'I'll show it to my lawyer and see what he suggests. Oh God, Laura, I'm so sorry you're getting caught up in all this.'

'They'd have gone after me anyway,' I replied. 'And I would've been alone.'

He squeezed my hand and we took the lift to his flat, but neither of us slept a wink. At dawn, when we'd given up on getting any rest, Frank went back downstairs. Whoever it was who was blackmailing us had left another card. It suggested an address in Soho, a few doors from my bedsit – coincidence or not, I never knew.

Frank's lawyer said there wasn't much he could do with just these typewritten cards for evidence, beyond going to the police. The cops probably *would* take it seriously, he thought, and they may well turn up at the specified time and place and arrest the blackmailer – but that still left us at the risk of being investigated for gross indecency or whatever the old Bill fancied, and the newspapers running a piece about us out of spite. Frank looked through his accounts: he could just about afford the ransom without having to ask his father for support, but it would make things tough until the London branch was up and running. No more ballrooms, and no more fine dining.

I insisted that Frank did not go to meet whoever it was, and for the first time since I fled New York, I wished I was still in touch with some of the heavies. Derek sent a couple of his more intimidating friends – neither he nor Frank ever told me exactly who they were, or who they met, but they got a result: an agreement was reached whereby our extortionist's representative could either drop his demand, or spend his £50 on a taxi home from outer London and a new set of teeth. Wisely, he chose the former, but we still didn't know if the bomb would drop. Now more than ever, said Frank, it might be a good idea to get out of the city, at least until the heat was off, and I agreed – but where could we go?

*

Nowhere was the grimly inevitable answer. It wasn't out of the question for Frank to return to India, but he didn't fancy explaining to his family that *I* was the reason when they'd struggled so hard to accept *his* sex change. Besides, we had no idea what I would do there. (Frank wore a huge grin when he suggested I be his secretary, but I wasn't entirely sure it was a joke.) It *was* out of the question for me to return to New York, even if Frank cleared my debts, and my only other option – the Paris of Toni April, Coccinelle and *Le Carousel* – didn't work for Frank, who wanted to be at one of his business centres, either Calcutta or London, or at least somewhere close to London. Neither of us fancied the commute from the suburbs, let alone the stifling life among the gossipers and curtain-twitchers, so we had to stay put.

The easiest and safest way to support myself, and the only one that tabloid exposure would not destroy, would have been to go back to the clubs. But after the Coronation and the 'clean-up' that came with it, there wasn't a scene in London like the ones in Paris or New York – drag acts were fine for our brave boys in the colonies during the war, but not the upstanding new society presided over by our dear Queen Liz. (It turned out that Frank *didn't* know her; my tactic of getting him to ask for favours had its limits.) The papers were full of articles about how to root out 'Evil Men', and the trial of Lord Montagu, Pitt-Rivers and Wildeblood was fresh in the memory. If the police saw a man in a frock in a car around Soho, they'd pull him over, tell him to get out and then arrest him for soliciting, and demand money to drop the charges. My friend Mary got arrested in Covent Garden just for wearing a blouse with stockings and heels. She told the rozzers that she was on hormones from the Marylebone Clinic, showing them an article about Roberta Cowell that she kept in her bag in case she had to explain herself in such an emergency, and got away with nothing worse than a night in the cells and a scurrilous little feature in the *News of the World*. I was scared to go to the bars, pubs and clubs, especially with Frank – he had legally changed his birth certificate, but I hadn't, so officially we were a 'male' couple – and they didn't want to admit 'obvious queens'. There was nothing more obvious than performing, so there was no circuit.

It took us a fortnight to work all that out, during which time the exposé *still* hadn't hit – nobody had even contacted us about it. Neither of us were sleeping: I wondered if it might be the best thing for both of us if the worst happened, as it may not prove as bad as we feared, and might even be a huge relief. Frank focused on the boring but necessary parts of the business, putting out adverts for staff, raising invoices, things that didn't form too much of a distraction, but that he probably wouldn't mess up if his mind were elsewhere. I got on with my modelling – if I looked like I was drifting, the photographers would click their fingers before they clicked their buttons. Learning my handful of lines for *All Over the*

Shop was a little harder, and Frank spent several evenings drumming them into me, trying to hide his frustration at my inability to focus.

'Perhaps they've decided not to do it,' I said to Frank in a secluded restaurant in Kennington.

'I'm not banking on it,' he replied. 'You might want to be famous, but I don't.'

'I want to be an actor. If that means getting famous, so be it, but it's not my dream in itself. And there's a difference between being famous and being *infamous,* darling.'

'Like being "flammable" and "inflammable"?'

'Not really.' I took a sip of wine. 'Sometimes, you're too damned dry for your own good. Too many Hollywood movies.'

'Frankly, my dear,' he replied, 'it would be too damned obvious to crack that joke. And besides – as you well know – I *do* give a damn. We need to find out exactly what's going on, or we'll have this hanging over us for ever. And it'll only loom larger the more successful you become.'

'You're not going to hire another detective, are you?'

'No,' he said. 'We go straight to them. Try to talk to them face-to-face. Maybe, once they see the lives they'll ruin, they'll think twice about doing it. To us, or anyone like us.'

I wasn't convinced. Appealing to the better nature of tabloid reporters seemed no better than getting the Keystone Cops on the case, and the more people we met, the more likely we were to be 'read' and sold. Frank said this was equally true of my modelling and acting career, adding that withdrawing from public life would be to let the bastards win. Perhaps we could find our man and discuss it like grown-ups, he insisted. In any case, I didn't have a better idea. Frank, at least, knew how to appeal to *me:* once I realised his plan would mostly involve chatting to interesting people over cocktails in bars in Fitzrovia, I reluctantly got on board. Our line was that he worked for a theatre company (although not as actor or director) and that I was a book-keeper 'who had always wanted to write', which was true. We insisted we 'didn't like talking about our work' and were more interested in whoever we met, which mostly worked.

Getting journalists to talk about themselves, and how they got into the profession (as I was ostensibly asking for advice on this) was never a problem; listening to them do so for hours on end in order to gain their trust was interminably dull. I wasn't sure if they were too self-absorbed to notice that we were transsexual, too polite to mention it, or if they sincerely didn't clock us, but that was a surprising problem – how could we have a sensitive discussion that would lead us to our man if they were oblivious to the core issue? Several times, we asked their thoughts about the nature of transsexual media coverage, saying we'd become interested in it after the Jorgensen story. Some of them lamented that 'these people's lives must be hard enough as it is' without this sort of harassment from an industry that claimed to speak truth to power. Some of the ones who we then told about our backgrounds remained sympathetic, even if they couldn't tell us who was planning to write about us, or how to track them down; others didn't, one even telling me that I'd had myself 'mutilated'. A couple just got up and walked away, and they frightened me most: they knew our faces and they knew that the names (and jobs) we'd given them were fake, and how to find out our real ones. Was this such a good plan? Had Frank just ensured that his inheritance would be squandered in an unwinnable quest to silence or sue anyone who might repeat what we had just told them?

Just at the point when I thought we were in too deep, we found our man: a freelance journalist called Harry Thurlow, commissioned by the *Chronicle*. Initially, Thurlow had hoped to talk to us, we were told, but someone tipped him off that we had been tipped off and then, fearing the loss of his story, he had resorted to snooping and then blackmail. Through our intermediary – whom I shan't name, but who was one of the kindest people we met – we set up a meeting.

'Maybe we should just agree to sell it,' I suggested the day before.

'You think *that* should be our opening gambit?' Frank almost shouted. 'Jesus Christ, Laura – I'm doing all I can, but sometimes I think you *want* this to happen.'

'Perhaps I do,' I replied, holding back my tears. 'I'm so sick of living in the shadows, being grateful when people treat me like dirt … Perhaps it will be better, probably it'll be worse, but at least it won't be the same.'

'Our first card is a cease and desist order. If that works on him, it'll work on anyone else.'

'And if it doesn't, I'm bankrupt and you're broken.'

'It's going to come out sooner or later,' were Thurlow's first words to us, in a dimly lit corner of a Soho jazz club. 'You can spend a fortune on lawyers, pay me off and then realise you've wasted your money, or play the game and take the cash. What's it going to be?'

'If we play your game, we can't play any others,' said Frank. 'That's the point.'

I didn't want to betray Frank by saying it probably *was* the only game in town, so I kept silent. His steel amazed me:

I may have become used to being trampled, but he hadn't, and wouldn't. So I listened, keeping a poker face as I could only be helpful by looking unflappable, as he told Thurlow how much he was prepared to spend on legal fees, and the quality of the lawyers at his disposal. Do that, Thurlow told him, and the peaceful settlement is off the table. We asked how much the *Chronicle* could offer. £250 was his answer. When he went away, ostensibly to go to the bar but obviously to let us confer, I suggested that we accept a story about me that didn't include Frank.

'I would have done that in the first place,' snarled Thurlow, blowing cigar smoke into my face, 'if you hadn't started spying on me. I didn't even know there were two of you.' Frank looked crestfallen, but he continued. 'You know, my editor is putting a lot of pressure on me. *Get their trust*, he said. *Then, once you have it, write it up as a couple of perverts trying to screw money out of the British public by getting their weird desires satisfied by the National Health Service.* Box-office gold, right?' He took another drag. 'We don't *have* to do that.'

'No, you don't,' I replied.

'It's a better story if it's about two of you. Half the people, half the dough. And obviously, I can't promise that your relationship, if that's what you call it, won't come out another way.'

'Another blackmail, eh?' said Frank. 'Why are you so bent on destroying our lives? Is it really in the public interest?'

'If the public are interested, then it's in the public interest. And believe me, they're interested.'

Thurlow stubbed out his cigar.

'I've made my final offer. It's up to you.'

All we could do was beg for some more time to think. Thurlow gave us two weeks.

*

While Frank went back to his lawyers, I began thinking about how I might make a living if I couldn't get any more acting or modelling work. I did my bit in *All Over the Shop* – the shoot was the day after our meeting with Thurlow – and resolved to keep working in the film world. Maybe those bastards *would* stop me, I thought, but I wasn't going to *let* them. I asked around on set, fired off a few letters and photos, and got Frank to chase up his contacts.

I carried on modelling, finding it harder than ever to keep up a smile for the cameras. Suddenly, the flashes felt oppressive, blinding me as their operators encroached ever further to get the perfect shot and trapped me in their glare. Nonetheless, I took on more – catalogues, mostly. It turned out there were lots of places I could work and keep a relatively low profile. Once again, Frank and I had stopped going out in town, or even spending many of our evenings together. When we did, they just became circular conversations about our conundrum, and by the end of those, we were too exhausted to do anything but collapse into bed.

Four days before Thurlow's deadline, we got a call. Another paper had got hold of the story, he told us, although he didn't mention which one – probably, said Frank, to stop us finding the journalist and starting a bidding war. I wondered if there *was* another paper at all, or if it was the *Chronicle* trying to put pressure on us, but it forced us to finally reach an agreement. I would sell my story on the condition that they keep Frank out of it. It didn't matter that we'd only get half the money, and even if Thurlow didn't hold to that lowly promise, it would cost Frank far less to support me, at least temporarily, than it would to take them to court, or deal with the potential loss of *his* earnings.

We told Thurlow that we were prepared to negotiate. Frank brought a lawyer, who insisted on drafting a contract. There was to be one article, and only one, which would just be about me, with no mention of Frank, nor of any love interest who might be identified as Frank. Otherwise, they were only to include what I told them – nothing from anyone I had worked with (although I didn't know what they knew about my time in New York), and nothing from any family members. Thurlow accepted, although he was adamant that £100 would be his final offer for such a 'neutered' story. We had no more than the verbal promise of a slightly higher fee, so we grudgingly signed, and I agreed to meet Thurlow the following week.

We met at the *Chronicle* offices, and I gave my life away over a tepid cup of coffee. I told him all about growing up in Coventry, how our house got bombed by the Luftwaffe, less than thirty years after my father narrowly escaped death at the Somme. I told him about how Daddy had disowned me long before I went for surgery in Casablanca with the money I managed to save from the New York mafia; in fact, things with him had never been right since I stopped going to Church when I was fifteen and he had gone to Kenya to do the Lord's work. I think he wanted more gossip: I wasn't going to name any of the actors I'd slept with, nor the performers or patrons at Club 82, and I certainly wasn't going to give him any leads. To his disappointment, I could not tell him much about Dr Burou and 'the operation', as I'd been asleep at the time. After a brief, tetchy exchange, Thurlow practically threw an envelope at me and told me to go home.

Three days later, the article appeared in the *Sunday Chronicle*. Frank told me to stay in bed. He had asked for the paper to be delivered, along with *The Observer*, and he finished making me breakfast before he went to check the letterbox, having promised me that he'd read it first, and summarise it for me before I got hold of it.

'Good news, darling,' he declared. 'It's actually quite *nice!*'

My image, modelling an angora sweater for a clothing catalogue, appeared on the front of one of the supplements, under the heading: 'LAURA MILLER – MY EXTRAORDINARY STORY'. Mostly, Thurlow had kept his word. No quotes from estranged family members or former colleagues, and only one photo of me as a boy, which I'd chosen on their insistence; no saucy exposés about actors or private investigators; and not a word about Frank. Indeed, it was framed far more sympathetically than Thurlow's cold, threatening demeanour had led me to fear, focusing on my attempts to live a quiet life after my flight from New York. They were even kind about my film work, letting me talk about my childhood passion for acting, and ask why my background should preclude me from working in the industry. For the first time in what felt like forever, we kissed: properly, passionately, perfectly.

That evening, Frank put on his finest suit and told me to get into my favourite dress, as we were going to celebrate something less than the worst coming to pass. Sure enough, the taxi took us to The Ritz, where at last we could dine and drink, and perfect strangers came up to us to tell us how we danced like we didn't have a care in the world. The next morning, I went back in front of the cameras, and now the photographers had to tell me *not* to smile. They didn't ask why I looked so happy, and I didn't want to tell them. Perhaps they hadn't read the *Chronicle*, and if that was the case, I wasn't going to suggest that they do, but I told myself that people *knew*, but they just didn't *care*. With that in mind, I wrote a few more letters in search of film work, and began to dream of Hollywood, or at least *Pine*wood.

We'd relaxed too soon. It had been naïve to think that we could keep any control over this, and within a matter of weeks, £100 and a night at the Ritz looked like scant reward for the levels of intrusion and humiliation that we faced. Reporters started turning up at my shoots, wanting to know more about how I'd stopped talking to my parents, how I got expelled from secondary school when I was fourteen and how I'd been arrested for 'impersonating a female' when I was eighteen – I guessed my brother had realised he'd never have a better chance to make a few quid out of me, and soon enough, he was doing a full-page interview with the *Picture Post*. All this fuss over an actress who (given that *All Over the Shop* was still in production) had never yet uttered a word on film!

The modelling work began to dry up. When it came, the photographers were noticeably colder, as if working against their will, and less keen to be seen chatting to a pervert like me. (One or two were far *more* keen than before to talk to me, but only when nobody was watching; they followed me around, certain I'd want to sleep with them, because after all, who else would ever touch me? The actors I'd been with went uncharacteristically quiet, although a couple got in touch threatening libel suits if I ever dared to name them.) My letters about acting work went unanswered, and after getting the phone slammed down a couple of times, I stopped making calls.

After the third exposé, I thought that was that. Frank tried to console me.

'People will forget about it,' he insisted. 'And I'll look after you while it dies down – you're not going to starve. Take a few days out, don't answer the phone or open the post. Get some rest, eat some good food and take some long walks. By next week, this won't feel like such a big deal, I promise.'

For two days, I followed Frank's kind, loving advice. While he plugged on with the London side of the Bolton-Taylor family business, I slept in, and then made him a nice, healthy lunch every day before strolling along the Thames or around one of the parks, usually Hyde Park but sometimes St. James's if I wanted to be closer to the royal family. (I thought they might have something to teach me about press incursion, but truth be told, nobody on the street recognised me at all, even when I took off my sunglasses.) When I got home, I'd think about nothing more than the dinner I was going to prepare, and Frank always made sure his working day ended just as I was bringing the first dish to the table. In its small, modest way, it was bliss. And then:

'SEX SWAP MODEL'S MAN USED TO BE A GIRL'

Nobody had even warned us about this – published in the *Express*, rather than the *Chronicle* (who kept their word about only doing one article, for all the good that did us). Frank came back from a trip to the newsagent, where he'd gone to pick up cigarettes, ashen-faced, and when I asked the matter, he practically threw the newspaper into my face.

'If you wanted more money, why didn't you just ask?'

'You think I had something to do with this?' I replied, once I'd registered the pictures of us both, and the headline had sunk in. He had his head in his hands, sobbing – he insisted that he believed me, and kept saying he was sorry, but he wouldn't let me put my arm around his shoulders, and just standing by him had no effect at all. Realising that if I didn't stop frying the eggs then I would burn down half of Mayfair, I went back into the kitchen, and stared at our breakfast, congealing in the pan as Frank yelled about how he'd never asked for this, how he didn't want people to know about his past, and how he couldn't face his clients in London or Calcutta now that this was out. I tried to console him as he had me, by suggesting that it would blow over and that later, *he* would be the only person who remembered it. This just made him worse, wailing and pounding his thigh with his fist. I sat next to him; he put his head on my shoulder and wept. I don't recall how long we spent like this, but it felt like hours.

I called up Thurlow to give him a piece of my mind. I didn't know what it would achieve, but I hoped it might at least make me feel better. No chance. He said – truthfully, I supposed – that he and the *Chronicle* had kept their side of the bargain: one story, about me, based on my words. Not their fault if other publications picked it up, he said; certainly, there was nothing they could do to stop them. He didn't have any plans to write anything else about me, he said, playing the honourable gentleman, and if it was any consolation (which it wasn't), it looked to him like the story had run its course, unless I landed any significant acting roles in future. (I didn't, and they cut my scenes out of *All Over the Shop*).

Frank decided that London wasn't for him after all. The business wasn't really working – he had already been struggling to secure premises for a store, or find a partner he could trust, and now he worried that people wouldn't want to deal with him at all. A week later, he told me that his family were going to sell the apartment in Mayfair, and that he would be moving back to India 'to help consolidate their interests there'.

The last thing Frank did for me was to book me a plane, leaving Gatwick Airport on the same day as his. We drove through Surrey in silence, Frank crying more quietly this time, me staring out the window as we passed through those little towns full of the kind of people who bought the *Chronicle*, who must have thought that between the twin threats of the nuclear bomb and the transsexual actress, their small, small world was about to end. I had a bag of clothes and the address of a bedsit in Paris, near Le Carousel, where I hoped to relaunch my cabaret career, away from the New York mafia and the British press. Frank's flight to Calcutta left first. We hugged each other goodbye, I watched it take off, and the next I heard of him, ten years later, again through the papers, was in a tiny paragraph at the foot of the obituaries.

THE FORGOTTEN STARS OF THE WHITE SWAN

This interview was published in The Gay Gazette *in September 1997, as the lead feature in a special issue focusing on LGBT+ pubs and bars around the time of the repeal of the Criminal Law Amendment Act thirty years earlier.*

In the late 1960s, just after the decriminalisation of homosexuality in England and Wales, The White Swan in Liverpool became the most popular – and sometimes most notorious – drag bar in the north of England. Nearly twenty-five years after its closure, *Derek Bradshaw* catches up with one of the performers who made it famous.

The White Swan looked like any other pub. Sat on the corner of Roe Street, it had unassuming décor: wood panels, wall lights and leather bar stools, white net curtains, and orange and brown wallpaper and carpets. Opened in 1932, it had long picked up punters who wanted one last drink after an evening at the nearby Royal Court Theatre, which had recently been rebuilt after a fire. Not that many theatre-goers wished to be seen entering The White Swan's mock-Tudor-style doors, however. In the 1950s, everyone knew the pub, not far from Liverpool's docks, was frequented by sailors, as well as 'pansies' and 'fairies' whose sexual inclinations could still lead to blackmail – especially from the police, who occasionally raided it – as well as public humiliation or even prison.

In 1957, the Wolfenden Report recommended that 'homosexual behaviour between consenting adults in private should no longer be a criminal offence'. Pubs weren't private, though, and it took another ten years for

Lord Wolfenden's recommendation to become law, when the Labour government passed the Sexual Offences Act 1967, abolishing the 19th century laws against sodomy and 'gross indecency'. Within months, The White Swan became known for its drag shows, as performers swapped lip-synched renditions of Swinging Sixties pop songs and sexual innuendos with the public's whistles, hoots and heckles – and sometimes worse. Over the next six years, it became an underground legend in Liverpool, known either as a magical place where almost anything could, and often *did* happen, or 'that bloody poofs' pub', depending on who you asked. Then, almost as suddenly as its cult status had grown, it shut down – rumoured to be heavily in debt to some shady characters. What *really* happened in that short time?

Kevin O'Brien – known to The White Swan's regulars as Mary Lighthouse – hung up his heels when the pub closed. Three years ago, he retired from his main job as an accountant, where he never told his colleagues about his second life. With his bald head and big nose, you might never have guessed, but Mary Lighthouse was one of the pub's most popular acts: tall, thin, and bandy-legged, with sharp cheekbones and a sharper tongue, she would raise the punters up with a sly, sexy rendition of Cilla Black's 'Anyone Who Had a Heart' and then slap them back to Earth with a carefully-chosen put-down.

'There were three of us who made that place great,' Kevin/Mary says. 'Davina, Ladonya and me. *The Liverpool Echo* billed us as 'the Golden Girls', and the landlady, Pam, jokingly dubbed us 'The Supremes'. Ladonya hated that: she kept saying, "I do one turn as Diana Ross, and that's hung around my neck forever?" So then Pam went with 'The Three Degrees', which pissed Ladonya off even more. But that came later – at first it was just Davina Delightful, performing on her own every Friday night. When that went well, Pam wanted to get a few more girls in – I joined next, some time in 1968, I think in the spring.

'My sister Tania talked me into going, the first time – my missus had gone to visit her aunt in Bootle. Tania and my other older sister, Gill, used to doll me up in their clothes when I was little, they just thought it was a laugh really. Because I didn't kick off about it, they taught me how to put on make-up and used to get me to sing for them, Vera Lynn or songs from *The Wizard of Oz*. Davina was on that night, on the tiny stage at the back with the purple velvet curtains. She wore an amazing little dress, white at the top, black round the tummy, with this chequered skirt, apparently a copy of one of Cilla's, and had this incredible platinum-blonde beehive. "Jesus, she's *stunning!*" said Tania, before she nudged me and said, "We should've got you a wig like that." I replied, "I think it's *real*, love," feeling jealous of Davina's little nose and cute red lips. Anyway, she did this Petula Clark number, getting all these whoops and whistles when she sang *Sailor, when the tide turns / Come home safe to me*.

'"Look at all those *flowers*," said Tania as these lads threw roses at Davina. "You could do that I reckon, they're looking for people." I told her not to be daft, I hadn't worn girls' clothes since I was a kid, and I wasn't a fruit. "It might be a laugh, though," she said. "I can help you." When I said I couldn't sing, she insisted it didn't matter. "Neither can Ringo, but they still let him have a go," she told me, before pointing out that Davina was lip-synching. Tania was a tall lass, about my height, so she had something that would fit. Hammered, I went back to hers and we tried it. She crammed my guts into this gold sequinned dress she'd bought for a hen night, and did my make-up. She kept going on about my "amazing pins" and promised to get me a wig, but told me to sing 'Somewhere Over the Rainbow', like I did in our mam's old living room. I could still remember all the words. Even before I'd finished, she was telling me to get down to The White Swan and ask for an audition.

'So, Tania took me back there the next evening, and demanded to speak to the landlady. Pam was pretty abrupt – "What's it about?" – and Tania was always bolshy, yelling in front of the whole pub that her little brother wanted to be their new drag queen. How could I let down all those people who stared and laughed at me? Honestly, my first thought was: "I'll show *you!*" So, Pam told me to be ready to perform on Friday night – I told her I'd only need a place to change and a Judy Garland record on the jukebox.'

Despite the decriminalisation, however, public attitudes often remained far from supportive of homosexuality or anything associated with it, and many people still struggled to be open even with their friends, families and lovers, let alone wider society. Kevin/Mary was no exception.

'Samantha, my missus, really wasn't happy,' recalls Kevin/Mary. 'She told me she didn't want to see it, she didn't want me to get changed at home, or the kids to find out about it. I spent the whole night convincing her that I still loved her, that I was straight, and that it would just be a gig. Then she asked if I'd ever worn her clothes. "Don't be silly," I told her. "You're about a foot shorter than me and half my bloody weight!" "But you would if you could ..." she replied. I just smiled, said I was "all man" and went to kiss her. I think if she'd pushed it any further I'd have given up on it, but she just said, "If it makes you happy ..." and then went to sleep.

'That Friday evening, straight after work, I went to Tania's to grab her clothes. Then we went to the pub. I got changed in the cellar then she did my make-up in the Ladies, it was all very glam. The thing I was most nervous about was prancing around on that little stage in high heels, I hadn't had much practice, just a couple of rehearsals with my sister on the Sunday. But I was doing it – Pam got up and said, "We've got something very special for you all tonight – a new girl!" And there was all this hooting and hollering as I walked down the stairs from the bogs, and Pam turned round and said, "Shit, what's your name, pet?" I'd bloody forgotten to come up with anything! So, Pam yelled, "She hasn't even got a bloody name! What shall we call her?" Some wag cried "Mary!" and Pam asked, "Mary what?" The bloke suggested "Whitehouse" and Pam said, "No, that's taken, you dozy sod." Another chap yelled "Shitehouse!" and Pam just went, "Alright, Mary Lighthouse." Just as I realised I had my new identity, I saw Davina at the bar with a gin and tonic, shooting daggers at me. But even more than the boozers laughing, her glare just spurred me on.

'They put the record on. I was so nervous, I forgot the vocals came in straight away. I also forgot I was supposed to be lip-synching and kind of bellowed the first line, and people started jeering. I wasn't a professional, *yet*, but I knew I had to ignore them and get on with it. I tried to take my mind off that fuck-up by staring at the chandelier – it was massive, I think they got it from the theatre – then I spotted

Tania laughing with her mate from work and realised I had to deliver the song to the people in the room. First, I went up to this Quentin Crisp-type in a suit and pink shirt with big eyelashes, and mimed *The dreams that you dare to dream / Really do come true.* He winked at me and said, "I hope so, sweetheart!" to raucous laughter. I just licked my lips and grinned. I'd forgotten how much those old queens loved Judy, I always thought of her as someone my sister liked, but I was really getting into it. I could see Davina had unfolded her arms and even if she didn't actually *smile*, she'd raised her eyebrows – she always had them done up perfectly, I can still see those little arches even now.

'I got to the chorus, looking up at the lights as I mimed *Some day I'll wish upon a star,* then as I approached the end, gave my hand to some old boy. I gazed into his eyes and mouthed *Birds fly over the rainbow,* then turned back to the audience and held out my hands for the big ending: *Why then, oh why can't I?* Everyone started whooping and hollering as Pam came back.'

'"Encore!" cried some old soak.

'"I haven't *got* any more!" I replied.

'"I didn't want any more *songs*," he yelled.

'"Well, you're not getting anything else, darling," I told him, to uproar from the crowd.

'"Who thinks Mary should learn a few more numbers and come back next week?" asked Pam. There was riotous applause. Despite Pam's dismissive "Off you fuck, then," I knew I was in.'

And so The White Swan's much-loved team began to come together – but, being new to the game, Kevin/Mary didn't realise quite how competitive it could be.

'As the punters went back to their pints, Davina took me aside,' Kevin/Mary recounts. 'She looked me in the eye and hissed, "That wasn't *awful*, but they're going soft on you because you're new." I asked if I might get paid. "For an audition? You'll be lucky!" I just laughed. "It's alright here," she carried on, "compared to most of the other shitholes I've done. I nearly got bottled out of the Southport Railway Club, but I don't think that'd ever happen here. We'll need to sort out your act, though."

'I didn't know what to make of that, so I went back to Tania. I decided not to get changed, and everyone in the bar was really sweet – I soon realised the bar staff didn't give a toss if the bloke buying a beer was in a suit or a frock, and nor did most of the drinkers, but some of them were *really* into it. The Quentin Crisp-type wanted to buy me a drink – I let him, and it was only later that Tania told me how disappointed he looked when I took the pint and went back to her. The pub was absolutely rammed for Davina's performance, though: a bit more Petula Clark and some Dusty Springfield, everyone loved it. She didn't engage with the crowd too much, although she picked up a bouquet that someone threw at the end of Lesley Gore's 'You Don't Own Me' and blew them kisses at the end. She didn't hang around after – Tania just turned to me and said, "What a bloody diva!"

'From then on, we performed together most Friday nights. I got more into it, and expanded my repertoire, sometimes taking requests. I found more clothes too: Pam introduced me to the manager of the Royal Court, who gave me a few sparkly dresses they didn't want any more. Davina told me where to get some false lashes and a nicer wig, with long brown curly hair, and taught me how to use make-up to shape my eyebrows so no-one at home or work would see if I'd plucked them. She also gave me a pair of falsies to stuff into a bra rather than manky old socks, telling me that "These are what I used to wear" before the hormones gave her "proper tits". I was told never to ask her about "the op" – April Ashley was in the news because of her court case with her ex-husband, and there was stuff in the paper about Ashley going to Casablanca for surgery. Davina was interested in Ashley, and I think they had a few mutuals, but refused to talk to Pam or me about surgery, and any punters who brought it up got a stare that could turn you into stone – or worse, if they really pushed it.

'Anyway, Tania came along most weeks, and my wife put up with it as long as I was back home, in "drab", by midnight. As the crowds got bigger, Pam decided to do it more often. First she tried Thursdays and Saturdays, then Wednesday, Friday, and Sunday. The weekends were always rowdy, Sunday nights a bit more downbeat. But it all went well, which meant she wanted to find a few more performers.'

Struggling to find people, Pam and Davina put adverts in a couple of bars around the north-west, as well as the Gender Identity Clinic in London and the Beaumont Society (a new London-based support group for cross-dressers and their loved ones). Neither got much response, because both the transsexual women at the Clinic and the transvestites at the Beaumont Society preferred to keep a low profile, and didn't often want to be seen with each other, let alone the flamboyant queens at the White Swan. Gradually, however, word got around, and Wednesday became audition night.

'We had all sorts try out. There was some bloke with a beard and lots of glitter, and a hairy chest in a tight pink frock. That might play well in London, but up here, it just confused people. One person insisted on singing rather than miming, and did a lewd version of 'Love In My Tummy' before hitching up his skirt to reveal that actually, the love wasn't in his tummy. Pam said it was "a family pub", even though I'd never seen any families in there, and told him that if he didn't scarper immediately, she'd call the police. He had to run off in his tight miniskirt and heels – I still wonder how he got home.

'The next week, Pam *did* have to call the cops. We had this queen, Lucille, who'd spent hours on her make-up and took herself *very* seriously. I'm not sure where she was from, but it definitely wasn't Liverpool, and she didn't like our Scouse wit. As soon as she started 'Break It To Me Gently' by Brenda Lee, closing her eyes and whispering like she was Maria bloody Callas, some bloke yelled, "I'll break it to you gently, love!" Standard fare for any drag bar, you'd think, but Lucille stopped and shot daggers at him. It was tense, until her boyfriend – some heavy from the docks – weighed in and twatted him. Suddenly it was chaos, Lucille whacking people with her handbag, lager and stilettos flying across the bar, fisticuffs spilling onto the street. No-one wanted the police to come – we all remembered the raids – but Pam had no choice. They didn't nick anyone, but said if it happened again then they'd tell the council to revoke our license. Pam stopped the open auditions after that.'

Instead, Pam and Davina scoured bars, pubs, and clubs in the north-west, looking for one more person who would give The White Swan its X-factor. 'We had a drag king from

Leeds try out,' recalls Kevin/Mary. 'He was great – doing Sinatra, Dean Martin and other crooners rather than Elvis or The Beatles – but the audience preferred the girls, so he only did the occasional bit. Three weeks later, though, Davina came back from Manchester with someone she'd seen at The Union, who she said would be perfect.'

This was Ladonya, a Jamaican immigrant only ever known to the pub's performers and staff (who paid their stars cash-in-hand) by her drag name. 'Pam was anxious about how Ladonya would go down,' Kevin/Mary remembers. 'I mean, our audiences were generally open-minded and good-natured, but everyone was white. We agreed that I'd warm up the crowd, and take Ladonya under my wing – help her with her outfits, tell her what to expect. We needn't have worried – she was a pro, quite well-built but with a soft nose and striking eyes, coming on in this beautiful lime-green dress and black wig, her hair styled into a bob with a side parting. She had her finger on the pulse musically, too, geeing up the crowd with Gladys Knight's upbeat version of 'I Heard It Through the Grapevine', knowing exactly when to smile, when to shimmy, when to hold up a defiant finger. By the time she got onto 'Baby Love', everyone was hooked, and our girl group had formed. Some nights it was just one or two of us, but if we were all on together, the place would always be packed.'

Entrance was cheap – just a few shillings – and soon, people were coming from all over Lancashire to see the trio. All three, but especially Davina, would perform across the north-west, but there wasn't much of a circuit besides a few pubs in Manchester or Leeds, apart from the Working Men's Clubs of Bradford, Huddersfield and Sheffield, which weren't always enthusiastic, or even friendly. The girls began to wonder if there was much of a world beyond The White Swan. Then a proposal arrived that was too good to turn down.

'Pam had a call from Granada, asking if they could make a documentary about us for ITV,' says Kevin/Mary. 'Ladonya wasn't fussed – she did care work with old people, and felt certain they wouldn't recognise her even if they did see it. I was petrified, though – I could ask Samantha to make sure the kids didn't watch it, but what about work? Who might it bring to the pub? Davina insisted on doing it – "It might get me out of this dump", she said to Pam, who couldn't tell if she was joking or not. None of us could, really, but she was always grumbling about seeing "the same old faces", though I was never sure if she meant the audience or us. Either way, Pam encouraged us to do it – even if it meant she lost her biggest star, it would probably put a bit more dosh behind the bar, and Davina gave the impression that she would either walk out or get me kicked out if she didn't get her way. I didn't want that argument: when Tania said she wanted to watch it with her mates, promising not to "out" me, that swung it.'

Queens of Liverpool was broadcast across north-west England on ITV on Wednesday 20 August 1969 at 10 p.m. – well after the watershed. It opened with a shot what 'looks like a normal pub', hinting at prejudices on the part of the producers, but then turned out to be fairly sensitive, as 'Pamela Watson, landlady' explained that The White Swan had a gay clientele long before the war, but even she was surprised at how popular their drag shows had become. The pub-goers didn't look they were at the heart of the 'Swinging

Sixties', despite being in the home of Mersey Beat, and nor did they dress for a revolution in gender. There was no drag or make-up on the men, or even the long hair of the hippies – they mostly had short back and sides (although a few sported sideburns) and wore suits, or at least shirts. The women are easier to place in their time, although they're more *Coronation Street* than Carnaby Street, and the reasons they gave for frequenting The White Swan would doubtless be similar now – it was 'a laugh' or 'a bit different'. More striking, watching it nearly thirty years later, is the variety of people 'having a good time': men and women, young and old, gay or straight, single or with a partner, even if the only transsexuals or transvestites were the ones on stage.

Most interesting, though, were the shots of the performances – Davina barely speaking to the audience, Ladonya encouraging them all to clap and dance, Mary having her usual banter – before the interviews, asking what their lives were like away from the pub. In line with her on-stage persona, and the Sixties singers who inspired her, Davina hinted at sadness and loneliness in her private life. 'Of course, there have been plenty of men in my life,' she said in her 'dressing room' – a dingy little office with a desk decorated with lights and a mirror. 'But sometimes they don't know I'm transsexual, and leave me when they find out. Or they don't leave, and that's worse.'

As she showed off some of her favourite outfits, she talked about a man she'd met through the pub – 'the great love of my life,' she recalled with a shrug and a half-smile. 'A businessman, 'passing through town', he said. Let's call him John.' Davina sighed. 'He kept finding reasons to come to Liverpool. I saw him several times, every other weekend, waiting at the bar, before he summoned up the courage to approach me after a show with a bouquet of tulips. He bought a bottle of wine and we got talking – all about him, how he'd always wanted to come to a place like this but hadn't known where to find it, how he wore his wife's clothes and his mother's before that, and how he'd followed all the Christine Jorgensen coverage in his twenties but didn't feel able to 'do what she did'. For a year, he would take me to dinner, to the theatre, to his hotel – all the most romantic places – but I never met any of his friends, and I knew he'd never leave his wife, let alone be 'more like you', as he kept putting it. And so it turned out – I asked him to make a decision, and he never spoke to me again.'

Davina wouldn't confirm if she was seeing anyone else – nor if she'd had surgery, assertively telling the interviewer: 'It's not your place to ask about *that*, darling.' However, she did say that getting an appointment at the new Gender Identity Clinic at Charing Cross Hospital had been incredibly arduous. 'I've seen it all, and had it all done to me,' she recalled. 'Doctors charging huge amounts for appointments just to tell me I'd get arrested if I went out dressed as a woman, sending me to psychiatric wards for stupid tests, then electro-shock therapy ... They only sent me to Charing Cross when they realised nothing would ever make me give up.'

The interviewer noted that the hormones had given Davina breasts, even telling the viewers her vital statistics. She just smiled, and talked about 'how much happier' she felt since starting on oestrogen. 'They wanted to put me on testosterone first,' she said, 'as if I should try even harder at being a man before they let me try being a woman. I had to answer *so* many questions – about my love life, my sex life, my friends and family, where I worked, what I wore, the works. I didn't tell them how many people I knew had abandoned me, but somehow it worked – I got my medication. They told me it could take ten years off my life, but I couldn't bear another *day* without them, never mind another decade.' Davina laughed. 'You should have shot all that, really – you'd have a far better programme.'

Next, the narrator introduced viewers to Ladonya, apparently 'known in these parts as "The Black Pearl" – a nickname that Kevin/Mary says was never heard in The White Swan, mainly because Ladonya would have 'fucking hated it'. Her understandable irritation at such casting aside, Ladonya came across as good-humoured, delighting the crowd with her performance of 'Big Spender', perfectly mimicking Shirley Bassey's struts and jolts, raising her eyebrows and wiggling her backside to rapturous applause and whistles.

'I don't know if I'm 'convincing', and I don't think it matters,' said Ladonya, interviewed as soon as she came off stage. '[*The audience*] love it, and that's all that counts.' Asked if she wanted to be a woman, Ladonya wasn't sure about that either. 'I thought about it before Davina told me what she's been through,' she replied as she put on her wig and make-up for another act, 'and I have enough on my plate already.' By this, she didn't just mean her (full-time) job, even though she often worked extra hours to send money back to her family in Jamaica.

'I came over in 1960, when they still wanted people from the Caribbean to work for the NHS. My mother kept saying 'It'll make a man out of you!' If only she'd known ... I'd just finished my studies at the University of the West Indies – I'd been there when Churchill visited the Hospital in 1953, and thought that if the British invited me, it was because the British wanted me, right? Wrong!' said Ladonya, drawing on a cigarette, before the show cut back to her on stage with a comment about how 'her style and beauty often confuse people'.

'I didn't have to re-do my degree, thank the Lord, but nobody wanted me as a doctor – or as a tenant. I tried Manchester first, and eventually got a job as a carer. I shared digs in Moss Side, but there was no way I could tell anyone about *any* of this,' Ladonya continued, gesturing at the rack of dresses in the office. 'If I came home with a man I could have been arrested, and I didn't fancy my luck with the cops than the guys in Livingstone Court. After three years I managed to find my own place, bought some clothes and tried out at a couple of pubs on Canal Street – I'd always wanted to do drag, ever since I was little, but I didn't really expect it to go anywhere until Pam and Davina showed up. By then, things had changed a bit. I could find a job in Liverpool, a bit better-paid, which meant I could support my mother and sisters back in Jamaica as well. Now the law's changed, I don't have to worry about going to prison, but I still have to worry about getting sacked. Or beaten up.'

Next, they showed her doing 'My Boy Lollipop' by Millie Small, but unlike Davina or Mary, she didn't interact much with the crowd. 'People laugh and applaud, but never want to take my hand,' said Ladonya. 'And I have to think *extremely* hard about which songs I do. I tried Sandie Shaw when 'Puppet on a String' came out, and it fell flatter than the cheap balloons I used to put in my bra. But then Davina did it, and everyone loved it.'

Ladonya didn't have much to say when asked if there was 'anyone special' in her life right now, and the documentary cut back to the expectant crowd, telling viewers that 'not everyone who does drag is a homosexual.' Then, getting changed backstage, Kevin/Mary told the camera that his/her wife and kids didn't come to watch him/her perform, and that for him/her, drag was just 'a bit of a lark'. Tania appeared in some of the crowd scenes, with a close-up of her laughing, but they had agreed in advance that she wouldn't do an interview, in case anyone recognised her and put two and two together regarding Mary Lighthouse's true identity.

'I regret that now,' says Kevin/Mary. 'She'd given me so much support and really wanted to be on telly. She understood my reasons, but I apologised for years. And looking back, I wish I hadn't spent so much time on the programme insisting I was straight, or going on about how I 'wasn't like' people like Davina or Ladonya. We got way more aggro from local lads after it went out, kicking off about 'poofs' and 'queers'. It turned out they weren't on my side, and definitely didn't think I was on theirs, no matter how often I mentioned that I was married.'

Queens of Liverpool was well reviewed, covered in the *Liverpool Echo* under the questionable headline of 'Fairies Across the Mersey'. It was repeated on national television as well as on Granada, and seen by tens of thousands of people – including one of Kevin/Mary's colleagues at the bank. 'I got in on Monday, after the repeat went out on a Thursday night in early September, and found a pair of size eight heels on my desk,' s/he remembers. 'For a second I thought, 'Great, I can use these!' Then I realised – someone must've recognised me. I started shaking: was I going to get fired? Or just hounded out over time? Who else might have seen it? Then Lizzie, our secretary, came over and said, "Surprise! Me and the girls are coming down on Friday!"

'Sure enough, there were all there on Friday night. They'd bought me flowers! So, I stayed *en femme* after my act and we had a girls' night out, with dinner and wine at the theatre restaurant. I got home late, wasted, still in my frock – I tried to get changed in the dark, but I fell over and woke up Samantha. She was furious but I told her not to shout because she'd wake up the kids. She managed to stop them coming into our room while I took my off make-up, and I promised her this would never happen again, but it didn't matter. There was one guy at work, Nick, who thought the whole thing was disgusting. He told his family, and his son was at the same school as our kids. Sara wasn't too bothered – she was a bit older, ten, and just thought it wasn't a big deal. Frankie, however, told me all the kids were calling his dad "bent", and one day over breakfast, asked the whole family what a "shirt-lifter" was. Samantha told him never to ask anything like that again, and Frankie wouldn't say a word as she took him to school. Samantha wanted me to quit, and I considered it, but what was the point? The damage was done.

'Tania brought her mates along more often to cheer me on, and the girls at work made sure I didn't get any more grief from Nick, who left not long after in any case. There were loads of new faces after *Queens of Liverpool,* and Pam put her prices up, billing us as 'The Famous Fairies Across the Mersey' – until we ordered her to stop, anyway. As well as more men chasing after us, we had some talent-spotters – in both cases, they were there for Davina. She started getting gigs in London – I didn't really care but I think Ladonya got a bit jealous. Davina had an absolutely horrendous row with Pam after she dropped a Friday night at the pub for one at the Royal Vauxhall Tavern in London at a day's notice. Pam didn't push it too hard – we all knew Davina was our star turn – but it happened more and more. We tried a few other people to fill in but like before, it didn't really work. None of them were disastrous, and the crowds kept coming, but we just didn't have the same chemistry.'

Not all of the new influx attended out of goodwill, however. 'At first, it was just a few wankers who'd turned up to heckle us,' says Kevin/Mary, 'and they got shouted down pretty quickly, often by Tania. This pissed them off, so they'd come back with their mates.' But the insults didn't just get louder and more frequent – they got nastier, too. 'People started chanting things like, "Get your tits out for the lads" at Davina, and when she ignored them, changed it to "Get your dick out for the lads". Davina wanted Pam to call the police, but Pam wouldn't, and it got to the point where they were too loud for everyone else to drown out with cheering and clapping. Ladonya got scared of going on – I talked her into it on one especially bad night, and people threw bananas at her. She ate one of them in a sexy way, spurred on by the regulars, and that shut them up, but Ladonya was livid when Pam told her not to react. She'd read about the riot at the Stonewall Inn in New York, and didn't understand why we didn't stick up for ourselves like that: she was apoplectic when Pam said she had to be more thick-skinned, saying, 'How thick-skinned do you people want me to be?'

'I managed to talk Ladonya into staying,' says Kevin/ Mary, 'but you could see she'd stopped enjoying herself.

Davina took Pam's side, telling Ladonya to turn the other cheek, and Ladonya nearly lost it when she heard them saying they'd both voted Tory in the election *[of June 1970]*. I told her I'd voted Labour, but she didn't think they were on her side either, and said she never would have come to Britain if she'd "known what it was like". I didn't know how to react.'

It came to a head one Saturday night in March 1971, after Liverpool had beaten Everton in the FA Cup semi-final in Manchester. 'There were people coming back from the match, and others who'd followed it in the pubs or watched it on TV, and they were all pissed and up for a ruck,' says Kevin/Mary. 'A group of them burst in while I was on – it was my turn to go first – and started singing, "What the fucking hell are you?" at me. The camp old queens yelling innuendos over my songs, I knew how to deal with. This lot, not so much.

'Ladonya was backstage, saying, "No *way* am I going out there!" but Pam told her that if she didn't perform then she didn't get paid. I told Ladonya that we'd look after her, but as soon as she went on, people started making monkey noises. I couldn't believe it – I'd been to Anfield and Goodison Park a few times but never heard anything like that, although, as Ladonya pointed out, I hadn't been there when Leeds brought that South African winger. Anyway, Ladonya just sighed, stopped miming, and walked off the stage. Some bloke screamed, "Fuck off back to the jungle!" as she left. Ladonya couldn't take any more: she hurled one of her shoes at him and then punched him in the face.

'Of course, all hell broke loose. The lads rounded on Ladonya – I took off my heels and wig and dived in to help her, and the regulars formed groups to take each of them on. Rather than beat up the women – including Davina, who stayed backstage – they started trashing the place, taking down the framed pictures of Mersey Beat singers and throwing them at people, sweeping their arms along the bar so all the glasses got smashed, and putting the bar stools through the windows. I took Ladonya backstage with Tania and we barricaded ourselves in the office while Pam called the police. They turned up and the hooligans legged it, although they arrested a few of them – one of the cops told us that "they never should have made this legal" as he bundled one of them into his car. There was loads about it in the *Echo,* the council put us on a final warning and the insurance wouldn't pay out.'

The White Swan reopened two months later, with a packed-out benefit gig that covered some of the costs incurred during the riot. There was a wave of community support that night, although the arrival of two new bouncers dampened the atmosphere and cut into the pub's profits. In the long run, crowds went down after such bad publicity, and there were other consequences too.

'Davina started playing other venues – new pubs and clubs springing up in Manchester and London,' says Kevin/Mary. 'There was more interest in transsexuality after the Ashley case, and *[travel writer]* Jan Morris came out. Pam dropped the shows to Friday and Saturday, which I wasn't into because I didn't get much of a weekend, and the kids hated it. Frankie said one evening that he was glad the place got trashed. That really broke my heart, especially as Samantha didn't back me up. But I had to keep going because Davina being away so often meant I was headlining. Ladonya wasn't happy about that, and had her suspicions as to why it was me and not her, although neither Pam or Davina blamed her for what happened, and told the security to be extra protective of her. Either way, the audiences missed Davina's glamour, and once she told Pam she was moving to London, I knew the game was up.

'We did a big farewell show though – it was Christmas *[in 1972]*. Pam decked the place out with tinsel, putting a tree in the corner with a fairy on top with Davina's trademark beehive. The pub was full for the first time in ages, Ladonya and I played support before Davina went through all her greatest hits, having some young lads dressed up as sailors for the Petula Clark number at the end. Davina promised she'd be back, and everyone went nuts, throwing glitter around and all sorts. But that was the last time I ever saw her in there.'

With Davina gone, Kevin/Mary tried to keep up the act, but found it too hard. 'Tania and the girls at work were supportive, and I was starting to get into it again when Frankie got sent home from school,' Kevin/Mary recalls. 'He'd beaten up some kid who said, "You're a poof like yer da". The headteacher said if it happened again he'd be expelled. Samantha told me it was the pub or the family, but by then, I wasn't enjoying either. The crowds dwindled after Davina left, the ones who stayed tended to ignore or heckle Ladonya and me, and I was about to jack it in when Samantha told me she'd met someone else – a 'real man' who'd turned up at her office. I tried to keep the show on the road, but there was nowhere to go, and I couldn't focus. I was all ready to quit, but in the end, it got taken out of my hands.'

On a Monday night in September 1973, when it had been shut, The White Swan burned down. The wood panels and leather bar stools were highly flammable, as were the velvet curtains on the stage, but the cause was never established. There were rumours that it wasn't an accident – some spoke of racist graffiti, which fuelled speculation of an arson attack, but nothing was ever proved. Pam, ashen-faced, went on ITN News to talk about how 'devastated' she was, saying, 'Everything's gone – the whole bar, the girls' clothes, the jukebox, the photos, all of it.'

'I never went to see the pub after that, I couldn't bear it,' says Kevin/Mary. 'I was certain Pam wouldn't try to re-open, and there were all sorts of rumours flying around – it was an insurance job, she owed money to the mob, a local businessman paid someone to do it because he wanted the space. I never believed any of that, but I was surprised when she applied for a new license. The council rejected it – they wanted someone to open a shopping centre around there, which they did a couple of years later. Pam said it was because 'they hate homosexuals, and they hate ordinary people having a good time' and retired.

'I retired too. I didn't have the heart to start again somewhere else, and felt I was getting too long in the tooth for it. I hadn't kept many clothes at home, but what I did, I gave to the charity shop when I moved out of our home. I cry thinking about that, even now – that little glare the old lady gave me when I brought them in, then the way she asked if I was alright ...'

That wasn't the only painful goodbye, though. 'I saw Ladonya one last time. She called me to say she was going back to Jamaica. We went to some straight pub, in men's clothes, but it was awkward – he didn't have much to say apart from how he was 'through' with 'this stinking country', and that he could probably find a better job and lead a safer life back home, even if he might have to give up drag. I don't know what happened to him, or how you might find out – no-one had ever known him as anything other than Ladonya.'

Kevin/Mary moved to Bootle, just north of Liverpool, to rebuild. 'I got a new job where nobody knew about my act, which I was pleased about,' s/he says. 'I kept in touch with the kids, even though I didn't see them as much as I'd have liked. Frankie seemed happier, and did alright in his O-Levels before starting his apprenticeship, and Sara got her A-Levels and then worked for the council. Really, I just wanted a quiet life, and I got it.'

There was one last performance, however – a benefit show at the Bar Royal on Wood Street in October 1979, staged to raise money for Pam's family after the ex-landlady died of throat cancer.

'I'd have done it anyway,' insists Kevin/Mary, 'but once I heard Davina was coming back for it, I got really excited. But I'd given everything away! No worries, though – Tania was happy to help. I couldn't quite squeeze into her gold sequinned dress any more, but we went shopping together and hired a couple of outfits. One was this gorgeous pink ballgown that I wore with a feather boa, the other a little black and white number.

'I recognised a few faces in the crowd – to be honest, they'd hardly changed, and when they cheered and clapped for me, it was like going back ten years. They went crazy for Davina, who was still just as beautiful as the day I first saw her. She did a long set with backing singers, costume changes, the works, and then we did a turn together at the end – 'I Got You Babe', the twist being that we sang rather than mimed, and that even if I couldn't sing, Davina really *could*. The New Romantic thing was just kicking off, and I asked if she might try to make a go of it, but she said she was 'too old'. And then she kissed me and said goodbye.'

The two remaining stars of The White Swan never spoke again. 'I read in the *Echo* that she'd died – it was 1984, I think in March. It sounds funny, given what she did and how much she wanted to do that documentary, but Davina was quite a private person, and they never said what she died of. I was asked to perform at the service, but it didn't feel right somehow. In the end, I didn't even dress up for it, and most of the mourners didn't even recognise me.'

One woman did, though, saying how much she'd loved Kevin/Mary's act. 'Suzie told me how much she missed the place,' says Kevin/Mary. 'One thing led to another and we started seeing each other. Just dinner and drinks at first, but then we went to Manchester for some shows at The New Union. She asked if I'd ever take up drag again. I laughed and said no, and she kissed me. We married a year later, and we still catch the odd show in Liverpool. They're much more professional now, way more glamorous. These days, though, I'm perfectly happy just dressing up at home.'

STANDARDS OF CARE

A copy of this diary of Sandy Payne, a transsexual woman living in Norwich in the 1970s, was given to the Norwich LGBT+ Project by her daughter, Simone. Her covering letter says that '[Sandy] wrote this diary during her transition, possibly as notes for a memoir. She never wrote one, but gave the diary to me on my 18th birthday, and I thought it may be of interest for your archive.' With Simone's approval, we have published selected highlights in this pamphlet, provided free to visitors, to give a sense of what life was like for transsexual people in the city in the past; the full text is available to researchers on request.

The Norwich LGBT+ Project, February 2020

....

Monday, 12th December 1977

Another letter from the docs at Charing X after last week's appointment, the usual about losing weight and ditching the fags before they'll even consider me for surgery. Apparently we *might* start to discuss it at the next one, which the girl on reception stonily said would be in *four months* – which, at least, is three less than I waited for this one – but if it wasn't that excuse it would've been something else. It had bloody well better be worth the wait, I still feel like it will be – I can only imagine how it's going to feel to look in the mirror when it's all done – but Christ, they try your patience, don't they? At least this time they wrote that 'Sandy is well-adjusted and intelligent', the nicest thing anyone's said about me in years, even after they told me off about my clothes – 'we discussed the patient's dress and comportment, which are not yet satisfactory for someone living as a female', as if some fifty-something in a cheap Mark & Sparks suit is the world's leading expert in women's fashion.

Dr. Randell said I could help myself by 'being more discreet' about being transsexual, as if I don't try and as if people can't tell. Every day here is the fucking same, grief from kids and glares from grown-ups, on the street and in the shop, Carrow Hill to Colegate. Some teen punk came into Oxfam yesterday, grabbed a size ten boot and chucked it at my head, yelling *fucken waredo.* Colin offered to call the cops but I thought it would make things worse; Joyce just shrugged and said *it's all part of the job,* which I'm pretty sure it's not, and all I could hear was Randell saying *it's all part of the Test,* which perhaps it is. No way I'd tell him though, he'd probably give me an F, the effing C, even though I'm only doing this in order to pass. (It's bad enough already that they ask me to doll myself up like April Ashley or Amanda Lear, it's hard to stay hidden in a city this small but plastering myself in lippy and throwing a little clutch bag over my big shoulders ain't going to cut it, especially when summer comes and my hair sticks to my head like I'm Bobby Charlton. I'd give them what they want but it's so hard to tell. Do they want me to be 'more discreet' or are they asking me to get into a beauty contest with Danny sodding La Rue?)

Most likely it was one of those little shits who march past every other Saturday on their way to the football, pissed up on special brew, and say they'll brick our windows if they see me again. If I quit then the docs will just make me find more voluntary work, going on about how 'you have to be in employment for three years of the Real Life Test'. I'd rather just stay on the dole, and it's hard not to laugh when I remember their line of 'It would be good for you if you could find regular employment', as if I couldn't work that out for myself, and as if I hadn't *told* them that every interview ends with a feigned smile and a 'We'll call you ...'

And Sunday with Simone, because Rachel was off to her folks in Diss – with her new fella, no doubt – and 'couldn't find anyone else'. It's no surprise Simone looks at me the way she does, the first thing Rachel taught her was that, 'Daddy isn't really a woman'; no wonder Simone keeps asking me why I 'didn't want to be a man'. I told her I didn't mind what she said but I wished she wouldn't come out with it in Woolies, I was just trying to buy some Pick 'n' Mix for her and a couple of new singles for me. ('Egyptian Reggae' by Jonathan Richman, the new Elvis Costello, and I thought I'd try Tom Robinson too – in for a penny and all that.) In the end, I had to take her to see the Christmas lights in the park, sit her down and ask if she liked being a girl. She said she did, and I asked why. She said she didn't know – she just did. I asked if she ever wanted to be a boy and she said, 'Ugh! No!' I laughed and asked how she would feel if people told her she *had* to be a boy, and she just went 'No, no, no, no, no, NO!' I smiled and replied, 'Well, that's exactly how I felt, except grown-ups didn't want to listen to me when I was your age. Do you think that's fair?' She shook her head, I smiled and took her to the department store to meet Father Christmas, I haven't seen her grin like she did with him for years, I made sure to take a photo because by the next time I see her, whenever that may be, Rachel will have made every effort to fill her head with more nonsense.

I wanted Simone to see her grandma too, but of course they're away as well, apparently in Yarmouth. *You must think I was born yesterday,* I thought, but still I said *Simone would enjoy that* and the line went dead, just like every other time I've tried to chat about anything other than the weather since the day I finally found the nerve to tell them how I felt – only once I'd got the Charing X appointment – and they told me to leave. They ignored my letter trying to explain (I wish I'd kept a copy, I could just keep re-sending it until they ordered me to stop, at least that'd be an acknowledgement). Now they only get in touch if they want something – and it amazes me that they still want to see their granddaughter given their contempt for her father, which I still am, and they still make a point of calling me in front of her, any chance they get. Fine way to treat your own flesh and blood and a wonderful example for the next generation, and they're always banging on about how the *kids* are rude. Maybe they survived the Blitz, but it didn't teach them any manners …

In short, I feel like shit, and the only people who even *might* be able to help – the Gay Liberation Front, that Society for transvestites who've stuck with their long-suffering wives – are 120 miles away, and Norwich is more likely to put a man on the moon than start anything like that. *Maybe I should just move to London*, but it's *so* expensive, unless I live in a squat in Hackney or Holloway, and who knows how much crap I'll take off people there?

Monday, 10th April 1978
Another visit to Charing X, or more accurately *Hammersmith*, last week. (Stop calling it 'Charing X' or move it back, I nearly went to the wrong bloody Tube.) After my blood test they're admitting, grudgingly, that I'm making progress on the hormones, getting more comfortable as my body starts to change even if I'm still pretty weepy a lot of the time.

They congratulated me on packing in the cancer sticks but can't (or won't) tell me if I'll get recommended for surgery, so I'm not expecting to find out any time soon. They had a go at me, again, for wearing trousers – smart black ones for an office job, I can't still find jeans that fit properly – I tried to tell them how I get far more aggro when I wear dresses or skirts, especially in summer, but Randell wasn't having any of it.

The best part was after I left Randell's surgery and argued with the receptionist about when my next appointment would be. Fair play, I suppose, I tried to trick her into giving me one in two months rather than the usual four and she saw me coming … Someone told her to 'relax', much to her irritation; I turned around, smiling, and saw that the voice came from someone reading the *NME*. She looked a few years younger than me, I'd guess twenty-six or twenty-seven, jet-black hair and thick eyeliner, in a ripped T-shirt with the name of a band, black tights and DM boots. I told her I hadn't read the *New Musical Express* for donkey's years, she laughed and put it down saying, 'Yeah, it's pretty boring', leaving it open on an interview with some new group called Generation X. I asked her name – *Elena,* she told me. Her appointment was late and I had nowhere to be, obviously, so we chatted about music. She'd been to a few good gigs lately, she said, bands I didn't know, Siouxsie and the Banshees, The Fall and Joy Division, others I've forgotten. She laughed when I said I liked Bowie and Television, telling me she'd take me to some 'proper punk' shows, although she was impressed I knew the New York Dolls – I told her about that chaotic show at the Roxy with their long hair and leather trousers, crammed onto that tiny stage with a hammer and sickle behind them. That made her ears prick up!

We swapped numbers and, to my surprise, Elena started calling me, laying out her problems with the docs, especially over – yes! – how she dresses. She was worried about doing her blood tests but didn't really say why, and just went quiet when I asked who was helping her through all this. 'I'm on my own as well,' I said, 'so why don't we go to that meeting together?' referring to that TV / TS Support Group advertised in the waiting room. Elena was quite dismissive – 'It'll just be sad old divorcees in twin-set pearls moaning about how nobody will employ them. Or fuck them.' I paused for a moment – she hadn't realised how perfectly she had described *my* 'life', but then she offered a half-apology, or at least said sorry. It was fine, I said; it wasn't really, but I got her to agree that we'd try the group if I joined her at a gig in London afterwards. Sounded like a fair swap, I thought, so why not?

Wednesday, 16th August 1978

I met up with Elena after yesterday's appointment – after I spent an hour in front of the mirror doing myself up like I was going to the Regatta, only to get wolf-whistled as soon as I stepped out the front door. Still, Randell deigned to praise my dress (one of the few nice things in my size that anyone's brought to the shop, and apparently the only thing to hit his sweet spot between 'feminine enough' and 'too indiscreet') *and recommended me for surgery.* Never thought I'd see the day! (I still don't know exactly when that day will be, obviously.)

I waited for Elena outside the clinic – she was late, straight from her job at the garage. Most of the mechanics were indifferent to her being a woman, after she waited months to tell them, putting up with them taking the piss out of her for 'mincing' and having long hair; once her chest started growing there was no choice. There was just one bloke who kept giving her grief after the initial awkwardness, but ever since he came up to her and said 'Get yer tits out!' and before she could ask if that was the best he could do, someone else yelled, 'Get out then Derek, you tit!' to roars of laughter, neither she nor anyone else has taken him too seriously. (I wish someone had my back like that at the shop.)

I asked Elena if she was still up for the support group. She shrugged and said, 'might as well', so we got the Tube to Highbury & Islington. On the way, she asked if I had any transsexual friends in Norwich. 'They barely know the *word* up there', I replied, laughing, but I did tell her about Sharon: how we'd met when I left a note on the board at CX asking if there were any others in Norfolk, and how she'd drive up from Attleborough for dinner in town. I got more hassle when we were together, so did she, as if the sight of us enjoying each other's company doubled everyone else's resentment. I sometimes wonder if I let all the looks and jibes damage our friendship, but really, I couldn't bear all those headbanging arguments about how 'only Maggie could stand up to the unions'. I said we had to stand up for the NHS – to Elena, as I had to Sharon – and recalled how Sharon would go on about how much she wanted to go private. Elena raised her eyebrow, perhaps to say, *I'd think about it, but I can't afford it.* Who among us could? We can't all afford to jet off to Casablanca for the op …

I asked her about who *she* knew. 'Not many', she shrugged. 'Other transsexuals always seem a bit scared of me', which I got (but didn't dare say). She'd been mates with a transsexual man, briefly, because they liked similar music, but ultimately, he didn't understand why she wanted to be a woman, any more than she understood why he wanted to be a man.

We got to Upper Street and it turned out Elena *did* know a couple of people there. Jacqui – 'the old bid who runs it', in Elena's words – gave us a slightly cold reception, Elena said it was because 'she's not into transsexuals', even though it was a 'TV/TS Support Group', but maybe it was nothing to do with Jacqui being a transvestite, she just wasn't comfortable with all these young punks showing up with their slashed tights and pink hair, effing and jeffing like the Sex Pistols on the *Bill Grundy Show*. Elena introduced me to Andrea, who'd apparently entered some mad beauty contest last year, her eyes done up like Siouxsie Sioux, fake tits in a Union Jack dress with platform boots, safety pins through her ears 'like something out of *Jubilee*' (which, Elena said, was a film they'd seen recently, with lots of punk people in it).

Here, Andrea was more restrained, but still in her fishnets, short skirt and big boots, which I could see Jacqui didn't like although she was far too polite to say anything, just being a bit more cautious in offering Andrea tea and biscuits (although Andrea still watched her Ps and Qs). It was funny to see these kids, who the papers are endlessly calling deviants, devil-worshippers or red terrorists, listening to their dowdy elders talk about how they were forced to quit their jobs and couldn't face the courts (like me), or how the clinic told them to get divorced so they weren't married to a woman (Rachel made *that* decision for me, I said), or got given testosterone or sent for electroshock therapy as if that would magically turn them into happy, functioning *men*. Elena talked a bit about how her girlfriend, Anna, 'called herself a feminist' but 'completely lost it' when she came out as transsexual, saying it didn't make sense that Anna 'basically hated men' but hated even more that Elena wanted to be a woman. Elena said she didn't try to save the relationship, and that there were 'quite a lot of feminists' who think like that, but it was the first I've heard of it. People were confused but sympathetic, especially when Elena talked about how she hasn't been with anyone else since, and when I said the same for me. They understood better when Andrea said she'd split up with her boyfriend because 'he wanted a man', and a couple of other people talked about how they'd had trouble at the clinic because they said they still liked women. We shared memories of our first Charing X appointments, all stupid puzzles and those tests where they show you an ink blot and ask what you see, but it got a bit depressing, and when they all started talking about clothes and make-up, Elena and Andrea got up, and I left with them.

Elena and Andrea were so brash as they strode back to the Tube, taking no shit off anyone, it was hard to keep up in my court shoes. They stuck their fingers up anyone who looked twice at them, but when some tosser screamed, 'You dress like my mum' at me, Andrea just laughed. Elena waited for me to catch up, and when I went quiet, told me I either had to shout back at them or take it on the chin. I sighed; she told me that if I let every comment like that bother me then I'd fall apart. I was feeling a bit better and then Andrea said, 'You *do* dress like my mum, though'. Elena smiled, then changed the subject, sharpish, telling me we were going to 'a secret gig' at the Roxy, someone called Wayne County with a backing band called The Electric Chairs who'd been in *Jubilee* and who, she promised, would 'make the New York Dolls look like Genesis'. *Quite the promise,* I thought, but I wanted to see if the band would live up to it. I'd got a bit bored of Johnny-Come-Latelies advertised in the *NME* with try-hard names like Dickie and the Glue-Sniffers or The V-2 Bombers with swastikas on their jackets to wind up their parents (not because they were actually Nazis, oh no). What would make this different?

A fair bit, it turned out. Wayne came on, holding the mic far too close to his mouth, snarling, *If you don't wanna fuck me then baby, baby, baby fuck off!* So far, so typical, but I hadn't seen anyone who *looked* like Wayne before – this huge bouffant blonde wig, permed, down past his (her?) shoulders, short dress and stilettos. He kept taking the mic stand, hitching up his skirt and sticking it up his crotch, pointing at the crowd and screaming at them. I was just stood there laughing as the thirty or so people in the crowd started whistling, screaming and 'pogoing' as Elena called it, sweating buckets. I thought I'd get eyeballs for not looking punk enough but nobody cared; it was so dark I could hardly see anyone except Wayne anyway – for one of the songs, he put on a hat and pulled out a toy gun to take the piss out of the police, crashing into the guitarist as he leapt around the tiny stage.

I wasn't crazy about the Electric Chairs' racket – a bit rockabilly, a bit punk, and to say they 'made the Dolls look like Genesis' was over-selling it – but I could've watched Wayne all night. But I only got about twenty minutes before I had to rush back to Liverpool Street, covered in beer – Elena said I could have stayed at hers but her 'squat-mates' had a band from Manchester crashing on their sofa. The next day, she phoned to say I'd missed a new song called 'Man Enough to be a Woman' which was amazing, all about County's 'transsexual feeling' and dropping the 'mask of masculinity', and fair enough, it did sound pretty great. Still, I'd seen just about enough to make it – and the pisshead lads shouting at me on the last train back to Norwich – worth it. The next day, I called into Our Price, HMV and Castle Road Records. None of them had ever heard of Wayne County, and sniggered at me when I tried to explain.

Sunday, 22nd October 1978

Last week I took my first trip down to London for something other than Charing X since God knows when. Elena invited me, saying this time I *could* stay at hers, if I came to this Alternative Miss World contest where she was going with Andrea. The first thing we talked about was the support group – how Elena knew it wasn't her scene, and wouldn't go again, but that I shouldn't let that stop me. I couldn't afford to keep coming down just for that, I told her; she said I'd be better off making transsexual friends elsewhere, maybe even at the event we were visiting. 'I'm trying', I insisted (but maybe I don't quite believe that myself) and mentioned how *unsupported* I felt on the Tube with her and Andrea last time we met. Again, she told me to toughen up, then asked, 'Are you man enough to be a woman?' and gave me a copy of the new Wayne County LP, *Storm the Gates of Heaven*. 'No-one's given me a present for ages,' I couldn't help but admit – she smiled and said the County gig had inspired her to form a band. I asked what she played; she'd been given a bass guitar by a mate in a punk group who said, 'If you can ride a bike, you can play bass.' They didn't have a name yet, she claimed – I told her not to call themselves anything too ridiculous. She just laughed …

We made our way to Clapham Common, where the pageant was in a huge tent. I felt really under-dressed – I'd turned up in jeans, trainers and a Bowie T-shirt, with no change of clothes because Elena hadn't really explained what we were going to. It was like a big circus and there were people in clown make-up, Elena was in ripped stockings and suspenders, leather miniskirt, see-through mesh top with no bra, her hair up. I have to admit I thought she was pretty hot, but I asked her where she got her outfit and it was all from jumble sales and Broadway Market … There were loads of people getting changed in the tent, I was just thinking I would've liked to dress up too when someone asked if I wanted *Ziggy Stardust* make-up. Before I knew it, a few girls spent fifteen minutes covering my face with glitter and gelling my hair up, honestly it was the most beautiful I've ever felt, not just because several (*very* camp) guys told me I was gorgeous but mainly because for the first time ever, Elena said, 'You look fantastic!' and *gave me a kiss*. She had a camera, so I got someone to take a photo of us, I hardly have any pictures of me as Sandy (and I threw out all the ones from Before) but as it turns out, I might never get to see it.

Andrea had turned up in this incredible get-up, basically poking fun at Ladies' Day at Ascot, in a pastel pink dress and hat with a fascinator, and a sash that said, 'Transsexual Beauty Queen', but with her usual fishnets and big boots. She was being photographed when Elena saw her, we were just about to say hello when Divine – the fat drag queen from *Pink Flamingos* and one of the judges – caught sight of her and that was it, she just ignored us. I broke the silence by asking Elena if she planned to enter any of the categories, maybe the 'daywear' contest; she laughed and shook her head. As we went to sit down, she whispered something about Andrea 'always ditching me if she sees someone more interesting' and then added, cattily, 'I'm not surprised she's come dressed for the races, her family are bougie as fuck.'

Then she started telling me about her latest Charing X appointment, which she thought might be her last. She'd been told that if she didn't start dressing properly then they'd chuck her off the pathway, and maybe that was for the best as she wasn't sure she wanted surgery anyway. She'd never go around calling herself 'transsexual', she insisted, and maybe she was happy just on oestrogen. We got talking about whether we'd met anyone since we last saw each other – we hadn't – and then the host, Andrew Logan, came on in this half-man half-woman outfit; one side an admiral's costume, the other a beautiful gold ballgown and blonde wig. I can't imagine how much effort it was to make (let alone *wear*) but it must have been much more rewarding than spending so much time trying to keep Randell and his lot sweet …

I doubt Randell would've approved of Divine's advice to the audience – 'Eat! Everybody eat!' – and I doubt she'd have cut down on the booze and fags at his request, either. The judges graded people on 'poise, personality and originality', kind of the opposite to Charing X really. There was a beautiful man in a white suit covered with musical notes; someone dressed as 'Miss Windscale Nuclear Reactor' in an anti-contamination suit (white overalls, black face mask and a Geiger counter) doing a robot dance along the stage; and my favourite, Miss Carriage, Linda to her friends, absolutely stunning in this mink neck wrap, chocolate-coloured shirt with a black train, long brown hair under a leopard-print hat ... I've dreamt for so long of looking like that, just for one night, but I told Elena that no matter how much she prodded me, I wasn't cut out for the catwalk. (To my surprise, Elena said she wasn't either, but I didn't quiz her further on that.)

The crowd were going wild by the end – the only other time I've been anywhere so full of love was Bowie at the Theatre Royal back in '73, everyone waving their scarves, all the young girls at the front grasping at his hands. When they announced the winners, the room was electric: they played *Land of Hope and Glory* as all the nominees (and there were a lot of them) sashayed back on stage. The clapping, cheering and whistling were deafening as Logan and Divine handed out the trophies, with Miss Moonshine third, Miss Proposition 13 second in a white wrestling mask and black catsuit covered in porcupine spikes, and I joined in with the roars and screams when they proclaimed Miss Carriage the winner, I haven't lost it like that in years! They played *God Save the Queen* (the anthem, not the Sex Pistols) and she waved to her loyal subjects, stopped to get her prize as people threw confetti onto her, stood up to thank the crowd and then disappeared backstage to celebrate.

After all that, I was knackered and wanted to crash. Elena said we wouldn't wait for Andrea, who would do her own thing, and that we should get a drink. We went back to the foyer where everyone was hanging out; Elena bumped into some girl she knew from the punk scene, who took one look at my face and sneered, 'Still into *Ziggy Stardust?*' I said, 'Yeah, what of it?' and smiled at her, she offered me a swig of her beer. A couple of her friends chatted to me about music, Charing X, the usual question about whether I 'like boys or girls' (*depends,* I replied) and what I made of the contest. I was too nervous to talk to Divine, but Elena did, gushing about how much she loved *Female Trouble* (I've not seen it). Divine complimented us all on our looks and, seeing how nervous I was, kissed me! Elena took out her camera and got a picture of us together: right then, it felt like one of the happiest moments of my life.

Perhaps I should move here, I thought, then told myself that London isn't like this the rest of the time. I'd still need a home and a job, and I'd be even lonelier without friends, because who knows if the people I met here would want to hang out with me the rest of the time? Then I realised Elena had vanished. I eventually found her out the back, necking that woman; they weren't happy to be interrupted. I wanted to go to bed; they just laughed. When I stood my ground, the woman said, 'Wait a bit, you can stay at mine' and they started kissing again. I told them I'd meet them out the front, where I stood like a lemon, watching people leave until they started kicking everyone out. After hanging around in the cold for ages, we got a cab back to this woman's place (Hattie was her name. *Hattie* the punk!) in the middle of nowhere. (Herne Hill, it was called.) I sat in the front while they snogged in the back, and the cabbie didn't know which of us to glare at the most.

Hattie had a bedsit, which we arrived at after 2 a.m. Rather than lie on the floor listening to them go at it like rabbits all night, I decided to tell the cabbie to turn back around and take me to Liverpool Street where I'd wait for the first train to Norwich, in another few hours. (Elena did at least give me a couple of quid for the fare.) I slept all the way back, it was lucky no-one stole my bag, the guard had to kick me off so I didn't end up going straight back to London again, then I walked home exhausted and went straight to bed, alone as always. I haven't heard from Elena since – if she wants to get in touch then I'll decide whether to accept an apology, but I reckon she's got people she's more concerned about than me right now.

Monday, 5th February 1979

Got back from the DSS to find two letters, both sent from London. The first was from Charing X, finally confirming the date of my surgery – 24th October. This came after last week's appointment, when I decided not to rock the boat by dressing like I was entering Alternative Miss World and instead to just wear, say and do whatever they wanted. Amazingly, Randell's sweeter side came out: he said I looked a lot better, not only because I'd 'sorted out' my 'wardrobe' and was passing more often (I said I'd not had so much aggro lately, but maybe that's because people look at you less in winter) but also because I'd lost weight. (I've been having one of those depressions where I eat *less*, but I didn't tell him about that, smiling like a good girl.)

Then he said: 'We won't see you again until after your operation.' I grinned and asked if that meant I'd passed the Real Life Test. 'I rather think it does,' he informed me, *smiling*, before asking if I knew anyone in Norwich who might look after me after surgery – apparently you need full-time support for at least two weeks after getting out of hospital. I wasn't even sure how I'll get back to Norwich, that train journey is going to be agony, but I said I'd work it out.

The second letter was post-marked 'Hackney, London' and straight away, I knew who'd sent it. I opened it nervously, and out dropped two photos and a bit of paper. In the first photo, the make-up sash down my face had sweated off a bit, but Divine had her arm around me, wearing this huge grin, and fair enough, I looked just as happy as I remember feeling. In the second, I was with Elena, our arms round each other, she was pointing at the camera, I was gazing at her, a little longingly, but still it was the nicest photo of myself I've ever seen. I gulped as I read the letter, despite her awful handwriting. It just said, 'Dear Sandy, Sorry I was such a bad friend after A.M.W. My band are supporting Sham 69 at St. Andrews Hall in Norwich on Friday 9th March – I owe you a pint. Love, Elena.'

It might've been the hormones, but I stood in the hallway and cried, at least until some woman came out of her flat with her kid and glanced at me. I'd been thinking about Elena a lot, partly because *Jubilee* was on in that new Cinema City at Suckling Hall (and while it was nice to see County again, the film is all over the place) but mainly because I've missed her. (I start my new job at Norwich Union next week, thank heavens, so I'm not thinking about spending much time in London.) I wrote back, saying no more than 'Thanks for your letter, and the photos – I had a great time at Alternative Miss World. I'm looking forward to seeing you at St. Andrew's Hall next week', and when I said I was looking forward to seeing her, I really meant it.

Sunday, 11th March 1979

Friday, fucking hell. I'm only just getting my head around it now. I took the afternoon off work and met Elena at Norwich station at 2 p.m. I wondered where the rest of her band were

– Elena said they were driving, but she'd travelled ahead to see me. This was their first gig outside London, and she was a bit nervous, but I told her not to worry, if she could handle crowds down there then she could handle them up here, where they're much easier to impress.

We went to the Cosy Café and got lunch. Elena asked about my new job. I said it was alright – they pay reasonably well and because it's such a big company, have ways of making sure no-one gives me too much grief, it's less interesting than my old job but I don't have to face the public, and it got me out of the shop. That got us talking about surgery, and what I'll do about being unable to work. I haven't told Norwich Union yet; I still don't know how I'll manage those months when I'll barely be able to walk. My parents still cut me off when they hear my voice on the phone, and Rachel hardly ever lets me see Simone, and obviously a six-year-old can't go to the shops for me anyway, so who knows?

Once again, Elena apologised for 'dumping' me at Alternative Miss World. It was okay, I said, I enjoyed most of the night and never would've gone without her. 'It's *not* okay,' Elena sighed, 'I promised I'd look out for you and I didn't.' It was in the past now, I assured her, telling her how I'd put the photo of Divine and me up in my cubicle at work. Changing the subject, I asked what her band were called. Coming up with names was impossible, she said, all the good ones are taken. They thought about Police State but didn't want to get confused with 'that twat Sting', as well as Profumo Affair, or The Sex-Change Superstars (Elena got argued down), but the singer had insisted on 'The Bastards of Christ'. Honestly!

'Hattie and I are going out,' Elena said, 'she's coming

up tonight.' I hesitated: Elena asked if I was happy for her. Of course, I was, I told her; Elena smiled, and I got the impression she was about to ask if I fancied her. I filled the space with 'It's nice that we're not *both* lonely any more,' and left it at that.

I went and made dinner, alone, while Elena did her soundcheck, then put on some old jeans and DMs with the New York Dolls t-shirt I treated myself to with my first pay cheque and wandered down to the Hall. It was way busier than any other gig I've seen there, although I've not been for ages, and I gathered Sham 69 brought some people with them. The joint was full when Elena's band got on stage and the singer, decked out like a typical punk in his leather trousers and ripped t-shirt, snarled 'We're the Bastards of Christ!' to a few jeers. Immediately, I knew this lot weren't going to be like the crowd at the County gig – not by a long chalk.

They launched into their first song, the usual three-chord racket; they could just about play but the treble was too loud, and I couldn't make out Elena's bass, let alone what the 'singer' was screaming about. It was boiling, Elena was sweating, her make-up was running and her five o'clock shadow was coming through. I turned and saw a bunch of skinheads in Union Jack vests or swastika t-shirts at the bar. These weren't the lads who give me hassle at the shop or even the hooligans I saw on the news, standing on the roof of the stadium or hurling shit at the cops when Manchester United came to Carrow Road. They were organised neo-Nazis and as I've never seen anything like that in Norwich, I guessed that they must've come up from London. They started shoving the women – and especially Hattie – aside as they stormed towards the stage. I moved, hoping they wouldn't notice me. They started pogoing, smashing into each other, beer flying everywhere, I saw the barmaid looking nervous as the fists came out. Someone chucked a can at the singer, got him on the forehead, he told them to 'fuck off back to Nuremburg', which didn't help. Then one of them pointed at Elena and shouted, 'What the fuck is *that*?' People laughed, she tried to ignore them, but they surrounded the stage – she held up her bass as a shield but she was trapped.

Elena tried to keep playing, and the rest of her band followed – they were *professionals,* these punks! Hattie looked terrified – I held her for a moment while I checked what the rest of the crowd were doing, it looked like there were too many skins for us to outnumber them. The barmaid was on the blower, probably calling the fuzz – I wondered whose side they'd take – but we had to act *now*.

It's funny, given how hard I normally try to avoid anything so threatening as a little kid pointing at me in the street, but I ran towards the stage – I can still hear Hattie's scream as I let go of her hand. I shoved through the crowd – people get out of your way if you're big, transsexual or not – and stood in front of Elena, holding out my arms. I heard someone yell 'Is that a man or a woman?' More jeers, more beer chucked at the stage, I saw the singer throw a punch at a skinhead and then it was anarchy, everyone in the audience realised they were going to have to fight these bastards. I could hear smashing glass as a couple of National Front guys squared up to us, I tried not to panic but I wondered if they'd pull out a knife or just punch us. They stood there laughing for a moment, one called us 'a pair of fucking freaks', ran his hand up his arm, clenched his fist, drew it – and then someone kicked him in the back. I kneed him in the face, hard, as he fell, Elena held up her bass and moved to smash the other one over the head, he looked around for back-up but everyone was fighting. By now the crowd were winning, there weren't as many fascists as I'd thought. They tended to the bloke I'd kneed and pulled him away – the Sham 69 singer ran up to the mic and begged everyone to calm down, they wouldn't be able to play if this carried on. As he spoke, I took Elena behind the bar and into the green room, Hattie rushed in, she had blood on her top but it wasn't hers. We locked the door: Elena and Hattie hugged, crying, I just sat and stared, catching my breath, I don't know how long we were like that but the next thing I knew, Sham 69 were playing, I heard the chorus of *If the Kids are United* but didn't appreciate the irony until later. I peered out the door: the way was clear, so I told the barmaid I'd come back for Elena's bass guitar later and we snuck out.

Elena and Hattie had planned to get a lift back with the rest of the band, but they'd got separated. I said they could either wait outside, or I'd put them up at mine. Hattie was too shaken up to go back in: I had my diary and a pen in my bag, so I ripped out a page, wrote down my phone number, went back, asked the barmaid to give it to the singer from Bastards of Christ and then ran out again, luckily nobody seemed to notice me. Then we walked home to calm ourselves down – no need for a cab, I said, it's not a big city. The only one of us to speak along the way was Elena, who just shook her head and said, 'I'm fucking sick of this shit.' Then we heard the sirens of the police approaching the venue, and quickly, quietly walked away.

We got back, I sat them down and made them a cup of tea. We were so wired, I got them to speak about how much they adored each other. Suddenly they were so kind, telling me how much I deserved to be loved, when the time came to sleep I offered to kip on the sofa. (Really, what use do I have for a double bed?) We never got a phone call – I guess the singer never got my note – and Elena and Hattie got themselves home the next morning. Elena rang me to say they got back safely, and thanked me so much for looking out for her.

Monday, 5th November 1979

I can't remember the surgery, but I remember the intense pain after waking up all too vividly. After a week in hospital, mainlining morphine, 'packing' the 'wound' to keep it open, not going to the toilet for days, they discharged me, telling me to make my way home. Elena and Hattie came to visit, bringing me the *NME* (with an interview with Jimmy Pursey from Sham 69 of all people, although he didn't mention the St. Andrew's gig), some grapes ('that's what you give to people in hospital, innit?') and a 7' single called 'Life During Wartime' by Talking Heads – Elena said 'It's not my thing but I thought you might like it.' They arranged for Rob, the singer in their band, now renamed Gangrene, to drive me back to Norwich; Elena and Hattie would come too, to help me settle in.

We spent most of the journey talking about *that* gig. Rob said he got a real buzz out of punching Nazis, I'm not sure he did much more than shove one of them, but I wasn't arguing. (Maybe he whacked a few after we left, but I think they actually got arrested, or at least the cops told them to piss off.) Anyway, they helped me up the stairs, Elena carried my suitcase, I was in agony by the time they laid me on my bed, the shooting pains in my vagina were unbearable, nerve endings starting to reconnect, I just prayed I wouldn't get any infections, it's quite common.

Rob told us he'd get back to London – to my surprise, Elena and Hattie said bye to him and not me. They'd arranged to stay in Norwich for a week, Hattie's older sister had a mate with a spare room, they'd both taken time off work so they could take care of me. While Hattie went to the shops, I showed Elena the dilators I'd have to shove in my fanny to stop it closing, Elena told me she'd decided not to go through with surgery, she was actually happy with her body as it was, and certainly didn't fancy sticking these rods into herself for hours every day like I had to.

For the next seven days, Hattie cooked for us, and Elena told me about gigs she'd been to in London and played me some new records. A lot of them were too full-on for me but I liked the Joy Division LP, the Undertones were fun, and Wire had some good tunes, even if I couldn't work out what they were singing about half the time. We watched some telly – mostly it was rubbish, but we saw a *Play for Today* on the BBC called *Even Solomon*, about this young man who wants to be a woman, who gets stick off her co-workers in a bank, more than I do at the council, and especially her pisshead mum, who's really mean to her for being such a 'pansy' – she takes 'Stephen' to talk to a transvestite about wearing women's clothes but 'Stephen' just realises that she's actually Susan and comes out as transsexual. Some of the medical 'facts' were way off but the way the doctor tries to put her off from coming out was spot on, and it even had a nice ending where she finds a way to be quietly content, I loved it. Speaking of TV, I couldn't bring myself to watch it when it was on in June, but Elena and Hattie *had* seen that *Inside Story* documentary about George/Julia going through Charing X – Elena had seen ads at the clinic a couple of years ago asking if anyone wanted to take part, she wouldn't have touched it with a bargepole and really, who would want Randell bollocking you in front of an entire country? It was too close to home for me, anyway ...

Otherwise, we gossiped a bit – Andrea was trying to get into modelling, apparently, putting all her spare time into it, but still terrorising Jacqui at the support group occasionally despite trying to keep her background quiet. I don't blame her, I'd love to do the same but this is such a small city, I think everyone in Norwich already knows but I don't have anywhere else to go, everyone at work just ignores it and sometimes that's the best you can hope for.

Elena and Hattie made themselves scarce on Sunday, when Rachel brought Simone to see me. Simone was clearly bored, we couldn't have her usual trip to the shops or the cinema. Rachel told her to talk to me about what she's doing at school and I never thought I'd say this, but it made me feel more *normal*, in a good way, taking my mind off the pain for a bit. Simone had done a drawing of me – she hadn't written 'mummy' or 'daddy' on it, but there was a bigger person in a dress holding a little girl's hand. I started crying and Simone thought she'd done something wrong so I just said, 'No, it's beautiful' and hugged her while Rachel went and put it up on the fridge. I wondered why Rachel had got back in touch – turned out her new husband also works at Norwich Union, had seen me around and told her to 'give her some company', surely enough time had passed after all. She didn't stay that long or look too comfortable, but that little act of kindness meant everything to me, especially as Rachel said to give her a call if I needed anything else over the next few weeks.

Elena came back in the evening with one more round of shopping, designed to get me through the next week – tins, stuff for the freezer, etc. Hattie made a proper roast dinner while we all listened to the Top 40 on the radio (I loved the new one by XTC). Then they hugged me, said goodbye and left, telling me to keep in touch. I laid on the bed and wept, partly because it still hurt but mainly because everyone had been so kind. I took off my clothes, looked at my naked body and asked myself if all this had been worth it and realised, *Yes it had*, and that I couldn't wait to experience real life again.

Sandy Payne is now retired, and still lives in Norwich, with her wife.

NEVER GOING UNDERGROUND

This short story was originally published in Flaming Creatures, *a quarterly LGBT publication based in London that ran for just four issues in 2004-2005. We do not know of any other works by the writer, who gave her name simply as 'Marina S.', and it remains unclear to what extent the work is autobiographical.*

Amidst the bears and dykes, queers and straights who had crowded Albert Square – neither as packed nor as passionate as it was twelve years ago, but heart-warming nonetheless – I recognised him before he recognised me. Perhaps, though, that wasn't surprising.

'Johnny?'

'Oh my God … Martin?'

'Marina.'

'Of course – Marina. Sorry, darling.' He introduced me to the man by his side, although I struggled to catch the name over the hullaballoo as a drag queen, dressed like someone from a John Waters film, daubed '28' over a Stagecoach bus windscreen in red paint. After several attempts, I heard that he was called Stuart. He kissed me on both cheeks, then asked Johnny:

'Is that the guy you used to go out with?'

'Less of the "guy", please,' I replied, trying to make a joke of it.

'He – sorry, she's – my ex, yeah,' said Johnny. 'We met when we were fighting the Tories. The first time around.' He scanned me over. 'You look well.'

'Thanks.'

'When did you …'

'Back in the mid-Nineties.'

'Congratulations!' Johnny offered. 'I hope you're happier now?'

'In some ways. My parents won't talk to me. Nor will my brother. Don't miss him, mind.'

'Seeing anyone at the moment?' he asked.

'No, I'm single,' I told him. 'I'm always single.'

'God, it's been ages,' Johnny said. 'Why don't we wander into the Village and catch up over a beer? It's on me.'

'Yeah, sounds nice.'

We walked through Piccadilly Gardens, still a construction site after the IRA bomb tore it apart, four years earlier. Johnny still held his 'Scrap Section 28' sign, and knocked on a window as we passed the bus stop.

'That tosser who owns Stagecoach gave a million quid to the "Keep the Clause" campaign,' Johnny snarled. 'Fucking Evangelicals – God can't take them back quick enough.'

As we headed towards Canal Street, Johnny asked: 'When was the last time you were here?'

'I moved to Bristol after my surgery. The Clinic thought it'd be best to start again somewhere else. I'm not sure if they were right, but I've made some new friends. I had to come back for the protest, though, for old time's sake.' Johnny smiled. 'You still here, then?'

'I'm a Northerner and I'm proud!' Johnny put his hand on his chest. 'I was in London for a while, working for the Labour Party, and that's how I met Stuart. But I'm a Manc in my heart, so I came back after we smashed the election.'

'Christ, it's changed around here. For one thing, the sign saying "Anal Treet" is gone.'

'Long gone', Johnny lamented. 'It's quiet now, but at the weekends it's full of hen dos wanting strip-o-grams. The shiny bars with the fancy salads are all for the straights. It's got even worse since *Queer as Folk* was on – so many tourists, and they're not all on our side. Some of the old guard are clinging on though – Stuart and I went for a drink in the Rembrandt last night.'

'That's still here?'

'Yeah. Napoleon's and the New Union are, too.'

'Do they still have the same drag queens?' I asked.

'Yep. Different millennium, same songs, some of the same punters. The ones who survived.'

'Ah – bless them. I guess they enjoy it …'

'Hey – you'll like this place,' Johnny told me, pointing at Manhattan Show Bar. 'It's run by that woman from that BBC *Sex Change* documentary.'

'Oh yeah, she's from round here, isn't she?' I replied. 'Scared the shit out of me as a kid, that programme.'

Johnny said 'hi' to the seven foot drag queen on the door, both the least intimidating and the most terrifying bouncer I'd ever seen – someone who would just as easily spike you with her tongue as with her stilettos. 'That's Truly Scrumptious,' Johnny told me. 'Or Ken to his mates.' Inside, there were all these young bar staff – 'trannies', Johnny called them – pulling pints. The one who served us looked about 19, she seemed so at ease in her pretty pink top, long brown hair (which might have been a wig), short skirt and fishnets, and immediately, I wished that Manhattan's had been around in my day. None of the tables were free, so we propped up the bar. Johnny's phone started ringing. 'It's my Mam,' he said, 'I'd better take this. Marina, why don't you tell Stuart how we met? And don't spare the details – no matter how gory!'

Johnny stepped outside and took the call. I took a deep breath, and for the first time in years, began to talk about those heady days of January and February 1988.

*

I told Stuart how my dad and I had driven all the way from Reading in silence. I always thought Dad had guessed, the way he didn't invite me to the football or the cinema like he did with my older brother. But he'd never talk about it, not even that ghastly line, *it's just a phase …*

Dad did drop me at Oak House, but he was off back to Reading once we'd taken my stuff to my room. I was the first to arrive, so he wouldn't have met any of my new flatmates anyway. They put me in all-male halls because I got my forms in late. Not my fault – they never gave me any – but I ended up with some absolute wreckheads. They did every drug under the sun – dope, pills, E's, whizz, you name it – and liked their lager too, Athletics Union social on Wednesday, the Haçienda on Saturday. It wasn't like that down south: the guys with crew cuts got wasted down their local, and the gays who spent twenty quid on their hair went to London. Anyway – this lot reckoned they were hard enough to hold their own at the clubs, even when every day it seemed like the *Manchester Evening News* had another story about someone getting shot, but really, the gangs only went after each other.

Immediately, I realised the only privacy I'd get was when I locked my door, and even then, I'd be expected to hang out a lot – so none of the secret cross-dressing that I'd done at home. In any case, I'd only brought my make-up. I wore bits of it – nail polish, eyeliner, mascara – just to test the water. Mostly, they ignored it. Rob would ask if I was into Bowie. He liked the Berlin albums as much as all that house and rave stuff, and made me feel a little less alone. Otherwise, it wasn't great – I thought uni would be talking about books, joining a band, getting into politics, but they weren't up for protests or even much discussion, and a couple of them voted for Thatcher in '87. *Maybe it was those Tory billboards saying that Labour would make straights go to camps with gay sports days,* I thought, *as if that would ever happen – bollocks to sport and bollocks to all the fucking arseholes who like it …*

So, first thing I did at Freshers' Week was join the Gay & Lesbian Society. Not that I really thought I *was* gay, but I liked men. Some men. Maybe I was bisexual. Maybe I was a transvestite, and maybe that made me gay, I didn't know. I just didn't like being a guy, and thought someone there might understand. However, I went on the first social and didn't click with anyone, so I tried to make friends with the other English students. That didn't work either, so when I got back after Christmas, I tried again. I found a flyer at the Union, and a couple of nights later, put on my make-up and got the 42 into town. I kept my head down as some scally on the top deck kept yelling 'Pete Burns!' at me. When I got to the top of Oxford Road, I asked a woman how to get to Canal Street, and she stared at me like something a cat had dragged out of the bloody gutter. Then I saw these guys, some with bleached hair and crop tops, and others with skinheads and leather trousers.

'Excuse me … do you know where the Rembrandt is?'

'Excuse me!' one of them said, taking the piss out of my accent. 'Welcome to the North, babe! We know where it is – but wouldn't you rather come with us?'

'Well …' I said, checking them out. 'Let's see …'

I walked with them, and they asked me how old I was, where I was from, the usual. They were going to Napoleon's, but I decided to stick with the Rembrandt. I'd never been anywhere like this before: I stood outside, trying to peer at the punters to figure out what they might be like, but you couldn't see through the windows. I stepped inside and cast my eye around. It was like the pubs in Reading – except with posters for drag queens instead of covers bands, pop instead of rock on the jukebox, staff who *didn't* stare at you like you'd come over at Christmas and pissed on their kids. They were playing Dead or Alive, *You Spin Me Round,* and as I went to the bar, these older men gave me the eye. I can't lie – it was intimidating but in a way they made me feel sexy, a little more than ever before, even though I didn't fancy them …

There was only one gang that could've been students – twenty years younger than everyone else. It was called the Gay & Lesbian Society, but something was missing.

'Is this just for guys?'

'The girls split,' I was told. 'They prefer the dyke bars.'

'And they're more into politics.'

'Maybe I should join them,' I joked. Well, half-joked.

'I wouldn't try that, duck.'

'They're *strictly* women-only.'

'Why?'

'Some of them hate men, a few of them really have it in for trannies.'

'Seriously? What's the problem?'

'I don't know. Apparently, the most 'male' thing you can do is cut your dick off.'

'SIMON!' said someone. 'That's *not* what happens, and

even if it was, that's bloody insensitive.'

'Sorry, Joanie,' replied Simon. 'I just can't think of *anything* worse.'

'Don't do it, then.' He turned to me. 'Sorry about that. One Bacardi Breezer and he's a fucking 'mare. Just ignore him. Like we do.' Simon eyeballed him, and he smiled back. 'I'm Johnny.'

No airs or graces, no sense that he was acting out some preconception of what gay men were meant to be like. Just a smart, funny, friendly lad. And *dreamy*, with his blonde hair and blue eyes … When everyone else was dancing, we got talking. About how his parents never gave up on him 'coming home with a lass' and how he split with his first long-term boyfriend who'd voted Tory. 'One of those self-hating queers,' Johnny said. And about how he'd been with his little sister in the only gay pub in Rochdale when it got firebombed.

Johnny gave me this leaflet. It had little bombs round the edges – his idea, he said, after *Capital Gay*'s offices got burned down and the Conservative MP for Lancaster proclaimed that it was 'right that there should be an intolerance of evil'. It said STOP THE CLAUSE in foreboding letters, above: FIGHT FOR GAY AND LESBIAN RIGHTS.

'It's not just that the Tories want us to die,' said Johnny. 'They want us never to live at all.'

'What do you mean?'

'They're trying to pass a law making it illegal to talk about being gay in schools. Or even have books about it in libraries. You're not gonna let them – are you?'

Thatcher's plummy, fingernails-on-blackboard voice rang in my ears. *Children who need to be taught to respect traditional moral values are being taught that they have an inalienable right to be gay.* I pictured my parents, and maybe Johnny's, nodding along.

'Of *course* I'm not going to fucking let them.'

'Come to the meeting,' he insisted. 'I'll introduce you to everyone.'

*

I loitered outside the Students' Union in a velvet blouse and a little mascara. Johnny jumped off the bus, beaming as he saw how many people were entering. I went to shake his hand.

'Oh, for fuck's sake, darling – gimme a hug'. He smiled. 'If this lot don't all hate Thatcher yet, they will soon.' He grinned at me, and we went inside.

All the boys were sat on the left and all the girls sat on the right. I noticed that while most of the girls didn't sit with their legs crossed, lots of the lads did, in a way that had nearly got me beaten up at school. Then I realised that the only time I'd seen lesbians was in *The Killing of Sister George*, and that was twenty years old. These were all T-shirts and trousers (but not dungarees, like in *Daily Mail* cartoons), badges with slogans, short hair, no make-up. I wouldn't have guessed that many of the guys were gay – there were a few obvious ones, older men in leather, younger ones in tight T-shirts with bleached hair, but otherwise they looked like the blokes I'd see out in Reading on a Saturday night.

'Watch out for the older ones,' warned Johnny. 'They might be PIE.'

'PIE?'

'Paedophile Information Exchange. They were bigger in the Seventies, but a few of them are still skulking around.' He paused. 'Or they might be the Socialist Workers' Party.'

'How can you tell?'

'Wait until they offer you a newspaper.'

As we laughed, two blokes piped up behind us.

'All the dykes keeping to themselves as usual.'

'Can still smell the fish though.'

Johnny turned.

'Did you learn nothing from Lesbians and Gays Support the Miners?'

'Minors?' The bloke replied. 'You're not PIE 'n' all, are ya?'

'They've shown solidarity by coming,' Johnny told them. 'We should offer them the same.'

Johnny turned back, shaking his head. Luckily, Hugh – the chairman of the North West Council for Lesbian & Gay Equality – started the meeting. There was dead silence as he talked about how one in five gay people had attempted suicide; about how Manchester's notoriously Evangelical chief of police, James Anderton, had described gay people, drug addicts and prostitutes who had AIDS as 'swirling in a human cesspit of their own making'; about Lord Denning, who boasted about personally sending gay men to prison before decriminalisation; about there being no mainstream gay press to counter this, and that Jack Cunningham, Labour's Shadow Home Secretary, supported the Clause, even though it was part of a Local Government Act that would strengthen the Tories by persuading bigots that public services should be cut.

Johnny stood up.

'The Tories have moved the goalposts' he said. 'London councils are simply trying to provide positive images of gay

couples, and Thatcher calls it "promotion of homosexuality".
If Labour won't fight her – we will!'

There was applause: he returned my smile, and then a
woman shared a story about her friend with mental health
problems.

'He had a breakdown and checked into his local clinic. They
asked him some basic questions, but as soon as he mentioned
his boyfriend, they packed him off to Wythenshawe Hospital,
slung him in a room on his own and told the staff not to touch
him. When I went to see him, they made me wear a gown,
like he had the bloody plague. And Thatcher thinks kids are
learning too much about gay people.'

There was silence for a moment, even if people didn't
seem too surprised by what they'd just heard. Hugh
thanked her for her contribution, and invited other people
to speak. A few more men and women got up and talked
about losing work, being disowned by their families, or the
pain of watching their friends drop like flies. Johnny could
see me getting sadder and angrier – he put his hand on my
knee and said: 'Tell them about your school.' I paused: he
looked me in the eye, smiled and I stood up.

'We got told nothing about sexuality,' I said. 'Every day,
kids at my comprehensive in Reading called me "faggot" or
"bender", gave me no end of shit for liking books more than
football, chucked things at me because I wasn't into girls.
People die of the ignorance this breeds, and no-one – gay,
straight, whatever – should stand for it.'

And there were cheers all around the room! *Whoa*, I
thought. Johnny took my hand as I sat down: 'That was
fucking brilliant!' Hugh told us how we could support the
campaign – flyering, writing to the Lords, getting friends

involved. There would be a march into town, a rally, and a festival with bands and speeches.

'Let's do this!' Johnny said as we left.

'Can we talk at yours?'

'Sorry love, I'm back at my mam's at the moment. Only way I can do my MA. What about yours?'

'My flatmates might be around, not sure they're cool with it.'

'What are they going to do? Hold a Straight Pride march? Come on, it'll be fine.'

So we got the bus together to Oak House. I told him about how my flatmates would say things like 'nothing against gays, but I hate the ones who mince about,' and thought that 'the camp ones' were 'a put-on'. He took my hand again, subtly, and said he didn't really get on with the 'ultra-gays' either. He said that like my flatmates, he liked his E's and went to the footy occasionally, Rochdale or Manchester City, but that their comments sounded like textbook homophobia.

'I think everyone's out,' I said as we entered, to silence and darkness. We grinned at each other, went to my room and shut the door. Finally, we could be intimate with each other, and Johnny put his hands on my shoulders …

'You know I'm a transvestite,' I told him.

'I knew you liked a bit of glam,' he replied. 'I didn't realise you were *that* into it.'

'When I was fourteen, my older brother caught me wearing my mum's dress. I thought he was out, and I was putting on her lipstick. The fucker took a photo and told me that if I didn't give him my pocket money every week, he'd show everyone we knew.'

'Jesus,' he sighed, sitting on my bed. 'Still – you're here now.'

'Yeah … I like guys. It's just, I've never said this to anyone before …' I sat next to him. 'I think I'd feel sexier … As a woman …'

'You want to dress up?'

I nodded. 'Just a few things I picked up in town ...'

'Well … first time for everything …'

I put some black tights over my shaved legs and boxers. Johnny helped me put on a cheap bra, which I filled with socks. Then he helped me pull a purple dress over my body, and I stood in front of the mirror and fitted a long brown wig from Affleck's Palace.

'Will you do my lips?' I asked.

'What's the point?' He kissed me, and then picked up my lipstick and did it anyway. 'Gorgeous, darling. Now, what's your name?'

'Mesmerelda,' I told him, laughing awkwardly as he practically doubled up.

'Mesme-RELDA!' He screamed. 'Are you angling for a slot at Napoleon's?'

'Okay, it's a funny name, but I'm not a drag queen. I'm not even sure if I'm gay.'

'Really?' Johnny asked, looking at my crotch.

Then he kissed me, and I thought: *Oh God, my chance has come at last* … But just as I took off his jeans, I heard the door. My flatmates were back from some club, plastered, screaming and shouting. *Just ignore them,* Johnny told me, and we carried on, but they started fighting outside my room – I couldn't tell if they were playing or not. One of them, I'm not sure who, shoved another one, Barry, and he crashed through my door, which we'd forgotten to lock. He collapsed onto my floor, looked up and me and went:

'Fuck me! That's sick!'

'What?'

'Look!' Barry yelled, pointing at me giving Johnny a BJ. 'Dressed as a fucking slapper, too!'

I froze. Johnny stared him down.

'Whatever, I'm out now,' I whispered to Johnny.

'Not getting up, Bazza?' asked Johnny, as I started laughing.

Barry muttered something and stormed out. Then I locked the door, and got back to Johnny.

*

That Saturday, we planned to go clubbing together. Johnny helped me pick out a new outfit in the Northern Quarter – black cocktail dress, bag and purse, size seven heels. You should have seen the looks on the little old ladies' faces when we got those! Especially when they asked, 'Are these for your girlfriend?' and Johnny said, 'No, it's for her,' pointing at me.

We went back to Oak House as I didn't want to get changed in town.

'What do you think of the pearls?'

'They make you look like my Nan!' Johnny laughed. 'If you want to be a drag queen, camp it up, but if you wanna blend in, calm it down.'

'Alright, I'll leave the pearls. What about the lippy?'

'Hmm – maybe a touch,' he said, dabbing my lips with some bog roll.

I didn't try to hide it from my flatmates – there was no

point now. They'd stopped talking to me anyway, apart from Rob, so Johnny called a gay-friendly cabbie, and we decided to wait outside. As we got onto the streets, these lads outside Gaffs started hooting and wolf-whistling at me. But it was worth it – we kissed for most of the journey.

'Watch out for Anderton's storm-troopers,' said Johnny as we walked towards Canal Street. When we got there, it was packed – the bars had STOP THE CLAUSE posters up, people were out drinking and if the cops had tried to nick anyone, they'd have started another Stonewall. There were more women than I expected, and no caustic remarks about *trannies*. So we chinwagged with the drinkers, downed a few in Napoleon's and went back to mine, spending the Sunday in my room, door open, with lots of pens and card.

Rob asked what we were plotting. I explained about Clause 28. 'I know, it's fucking disgusting,' he replied, so we told him to come to the rally. 'See?' Johnny shouted. 'That woman's gone too far – even the straights won't stand for it.'

'Well, some of them,' I said.

'It'll grow,' Johnny replied. 'Trust me.'

The next evening, Johnny and I attended the next meeting. There were scores of people going into the Town Hall – 'Told you,' said Johnny – and it took ages for Hugh to get us to sit down and shut up, it was so buzzing. Hugh mentioned celebrities who were supporting us – not just the usual ones like Ken Livingstone and Peter Tatchell ('Both good Labour men,' Johnny whispered) but soap stars, musicians and actors – Ian McKellen had come out in response to the Bill, we were informed to rapturous cheers, and he probably wouldn't be the last.

The first vote concerned Viraj Mendes – an asylum seeker

in Hulme, whom the government planned to deport. The radicals – mainly the SWP – wanted us to campaign on his behalf, to 'build more solidarity,' like with the miners. To my surprise, Johnny voted against. 'We don't want to confuse things,' he said, after I voted 'for'. 'More people will back us if it's just about the Clause.' So, the meeting decided not to campaign for Mendes – I forget the exact result, but it was a clear majority.

The next item? I knew what a palaver this was going to be when Hugh uttered the words 'Clone Zone advert' and Johnny threw his head back, sighing. Immediately, the room felt heavier; something had to give. As soon as Hugh spoke about how much money the shop had given to the campaign, I heard a woman's voice cry out:

'He looks like he's got a bleedin' pineapple down his knickers!'

Absolute guffaws – from the right-hand side of the room. Which was where, I clocked, all the lesbians were. A few guys let out a giggle, soon stifled by disapproving glances from the more 'serious' activists.

'There were separate meetings about this,' Johnny said.

'And you didn't tell me?'

He looked apologetic. 'I only found out later.'

They displayed the advert on an overhead projector. Now, the room was dominated by a huge image of a bloke in his Y-fronts, with a boner the size of the Free Trade Hall, scheduled to feature prominently in the Festival programme. You couldn't help but laugh – a cacophony of voices screaming things like:

'They've given us so much support!'

'They can support us without waving their giant dicks in

everyone's faces!'

'It's about having a right to our sexuality!'

'Your sexuality! What about ours?'

'This is supposed to be about gay and lesbian rights, not bloody porn!'

'All the banners say, "Gay and Lesbian", what more d'ya want?'

A man stood up.

'Christ! Everyone CALM DOWN! Fuck me!' The projector was turned off and the sniping fell silent. 'I remember before 1967,' he said. 'Before decriminalisation. People thought that gay men were predators, potential rapists, obsessed with sex. Lots still think that – listen to what's coming out of the Tory Party, or the flaming Manchester police. I know we need to stand up to them, but this sort of thing will only give them ammunition.'

Hugh banged the table.

'We need to settle this democratically. All those in favour of keeping the Clone Zone advert, put up your hands.'

Johnny's arm shot up.

'We need to be able to celebrate our sexuality,' said Johnny. 'Otherwise, why are we here?'

'And those against?'

Tentatively, I raised my hand – along with everyone on the right-hand side, and a few on ours.

'If the women don't feel welcome, it's not their movement,' I whispered. 'And I don't think it's worth alienating them over this.'

A voice behind me interjected: 'You what?'

Hugh asked for abstentions, and then announced that the advert would not be used. There were cheers from the women, and a few murmurs from the men. Johnny gave me a half-smile, eyebrows raised. I took his hand, and we moved on to the final item.

'Andy Bell and Jimmy Somerville wish to perform at the Festival in drag. Some on the Committee feel this could confuse the issues around sexuality, and these sort of drag shows are demeaning to women. We are sure that they'll accept our invitation even if we would prefer–'

'If we pulled the advert on grounds of taste,' someone butted in, 'we should pull this too.'

'Wait!' Hugh continued. 'Others felt that we shouldn't censor anyone's sexuality, however they want to express it – otherwise we're as bad as the government-'

'But the tabloids will have a field day!'

I stood up.

'Look, it's simple. We respected the women's opinion on the advert, and we should respect the transsexuals' opinion on this.'

'There *aren't* any bloody transsexuals,' a bloke yelled.

'Why not?' I asked.

'Maybe they're just not interested,' a woman answered.

'If there are any transsexuals here, please raise your hands,' came a voice from in front of us.

'For fuck's sake,' shouted Johnny. 'It's not a bleeding witch hunt.'

'All those who think Bell and Somerville should *not* perform in drag, please raise your hands.'

Most of the room put up their arms. I didn't, and nor did Johnny. I slumped into my chair.

'Sorry, darling. But if we respected the decision on everything else …'

I sighed as Hugh passed the motion and concluded the

meeting. As we left, a woman came up to me. She was a bit older than most people there, slightly dowdy, softly spoken.

'Hi, I'm Philippa. I just wanted to thank you for speaking up.' There was an awkward silence. 'If you're interested, our group meets every other Thursday. Maybe I'll see you there.'

She handed me a card, headed 'TV/TS Support Centre', with a PO Box address and a phone number. I thanked her, and she walked away. I kissed Johnny on the cheek and got the bus back to Oak House, alone, trying not to cry.

*

We found each other outside Jilly's Rockworld, Philippa and I, slightly ahead of time. As the marchers strode into view, sometime after we heard the claps, cheers, whistles, even drummers and saxophonists on the horizon, the chants of 'We're here! We're queer! We're not going shopping!' she asked if we were waiting for my boyfriend.

'We decided to meet for the festival,' I told her.

'Oh ... what's up?'

'The last meeting. I don't think he got why I was so upset about the Bell and Somerville thing.'

'Why? You're not a drag queen, are you?'

'Well ... no ... But I thought he'd understand why I didn't think it was fair ...'

'Maybe it's for the best,' sighed Philippa. 'Maybe they'd make everyone look ridiculous.'

'Yeah, maybe.'

We let ourselves be sucked into the surging crowd, seeing men hold hands in the street, lesbian couples with children, handwritten signs demanding EQUAL RIGHTS NOW, or declaring that LESBIAN AND GAY RIGHTS ARE HUMAN RIGHTS, that WE'RE OUT AND WE'RE STAYING OUT, SWP placards and banners of groups from Bradford, London, Newcastle that had joined us. I held up my NEVER GOING UNDERGROUND logo and walked along the fringes, earnestly.

'Give us a smile, love!' A stranger accosted me. 'I know it's a protest, but you can still have fun!'

I struggled to turn my lips upwards, unconvincingly, and then turned to Philippa.

'Johnny doesn't fancy me as a woman. He said it was fun once, but it doesn't turn him on.'

'He's a gay man – what do you expect?'

'This is more important to him right now.' I waved my hand across the crowd. 'He says he can't concentrate on a relationship. Maybe we'll work things out, but …'

But I couldn't help but join in the chant: 'What do we want? Equal rights! When do we want them? Now!' We turned onto Albert Square, just as one of the organisers, Kürşad Karamanoğlu, stoked up the audience: 'If London is New York, then welcome to San Francisco!'

'Christ alive,' said Philippa. 'Look!'

It was astounding, pulsating crowds as far as the eye could see, some listening attentively, others cheering and whooping as a man with a megaphone proudly told us that twenty thousand people had attended. I clapped along as we were told this was the largest national demonstration in Manchester in the last twenty years, and that the police 'were not the most numerate' as they had planned for fifteen thousand. 'Stick that in your stupid pipe and suck it, Anderton!' I heard as Philippa and I tried to push towards the front. Then, under the Manchester University Gay &

Lesbians Students banner, a familiar voice: 'I tried to tell this kid in my Maths class when I was 14 that I fancied him, but I bottled it. Probably would've got my head kicked in anyway–'

I tapped his shoulder.

'Mesmerelda?'

'I prefer Marina now.'

'Well – I'm so happy to see you, Marina!'

To my surprise, he gave me a massive hug, but I knew from the way that he kissed my cheek that things weren't quite the same.

'This is incredible! We even got a Labour councillor to stick his neck out!'

He joined the applause as Michael Cashman from *EastEnders* came on and shouted, 'I'm here … because I'm proud!' He was jumping up and down, embracing everyone around him, almost hyperventilating – I'd never seen anyone so ecstatic. So we stayed together as Cashman talked about 'ordinary men and women made extraordinary by society's focus on what we do in bed.' It was inspirational, really, to see so many people agreeing with him, all of whom fell quiet as he talked about how people could gas or shoot us, but that so long as people continued to procreate, homosexuality would exist. Then, two actors from *Brookside* came on, well received despite playing Scousers: Sue Johnston compared the clause to the Nazi book-burning, before Steve Parry screamed: 'Who the hell is going to get a closet big enough for all of us?'

'There bloody well ain't any n'all,' beamed Johnny, putting his arm around me.

'Not once most of you are out,' I said.

'What do you mean?' he asked. 'You're out now, aren't you?'

'I don't *feel* out,' I replied. 'Not really.'

'Do you want to be a woman?'

'Maybe. I don't know. Perhaps we should talk about it later.'

From his silence, I knew that we would never survive something this colossal; it might be best that we try to be friends now, rather than tear ourselves apart further down the line. After Philippa left, we spent the evening together, but I found it impossible to enjoy the Communards or Erasure as much as everyone around me seemed to, and Ian McKellen's recital of Thomas More, beautiful as it was, didn't quite strike me in the same way as it did Johnny. At the end, we kissed, but it just wasn't like the old days any more, and I went home alone – seeing Rob with his girlfriend when I got in, hearing him say that they both had a brilliant time at the protest, just made it feel even more bittersweet …

*

'So that's it,' I told Stuart. As Johnny came back in, putting his phone in his pocket, I noticed that Manhattan's had cleared out, and that the barmaid – who, she told me, was called Marlene – had been listening to most of my story. 'I guess things are better now.'

'Yeah, but it's still not great,' Marlene interjected. 'Some kids in a car threw a load of eggs at Truly a while back. They missed, but you can still see it out the front.'

'And the local rag is still at it,' said Johnny as he sat down. 'They picked out a photo of a couple of leather queens that Marketing Manchester had put in a brochure and ran a headline saying, "Is this how we want to promote our city?" Of course, they encouraged everyone to say no. People are getting scared to hold hands again.'

'Tony will sort it,' replied Stuart, and Johnny put his arm around him. 'The Loony Left might not have stopped the Clause, but he will.'

'Perhaps, but we did the groundwork,' I sigh. 'It's weird how these things pan out.'

'What do you mean?' asked Marlene.

I explained how the Clause, introduced to silence and separate us, had brought us all together, and how the campaign had led me somewhere entirely different to most of my comrades. I told Johnny, Stuart and Marlene about how I'd gone to Philippa's TV/TS group, which had met in Canal Street, until I moved away, and how they had supported me when my parents disowned me, and when old friends like Rob from halls turned their backs on me.

Marlene in particular looked apprehensive, and I didn't want to leave her on that note.

'Now, things are ...' I hesitated. 'I don't know if they're better, but they're not getting worse. I guess they're just different.'

'And they'll change more once we finally get rid of Maggie's law," replied Stuart

Johnny smiled, and hugged me nearly as hard as he had when we'd first met outside the Student Union. 'It's been so wonderful seeing you again. Keep in touch, yeah? Stuart and I have bought a flat just round the corner – come and stay whenever you like.'

'Absolutely. And if you're ever in Bristol – feel free to do the same.'

I watched Johnny and Stuart leave, hand in hand, and then saw that Marlene had brought over another gin and tonic. I asked if it was for me: she said it was, and shook her head, smiling, when I reached into my handbag. Seeing that all the other drinkers had left, she sat with me and gave me a little of her life. She told me about how her parents didn't know about her cross-dressing, which had started when she was seven, and that she was terrified of them finding out, or having to tell them. She explained that she got hassle when she dressed as a woman in public, and often got changed at the bar for her shifts, but that she'd found a couple of friends who took her shopping, helped her learn about make-up and keeping safe, and that they felt more like a community than the university's Gay & Lesbian Society, which had been a massive let-down for her. She said she was seeing a guy who was okay with her cross-dressing but preferred her as a bloke, and that she didn't think she'd stay with him much longer, maybe she liked women more. Finally, she didn't think she wanted to be a drag queen like the ones she'd seen at the Hollywood Showbar, just down the road, and that she hadn't worked out if she was a transvestite, transsexual or something else, but that my story had made her feel like it might be more interesting – and more fun – to work out than she'd realised. Then she asked if I wanted to stay for one more drink.

'You're very sweet, but I should really go,' I told her. 'Hopefully I'll see you again.'

'THE TWIST'

This script was submitted, unsolicited, to Sunrise, a British independent film company, in 2015 – twenty years after the events it depicts.

....

FADE IN:

SCENE 1. INT. ROBERT'S OFFICE - DAY

Robert is sitting at his desk. The room is messy - papers, film magazines and VHS tapes piled up, mugs left uncleaned. There are three posters, framed - Hitchcock's 'Psycho', 'Peeping Tom' by Michael Powell, and 'The Spire'.

Next to him is Emily. She looks nervous, in contrast to Robert's clear self-assurance. Interviewing them both is twenty-three-year-old journalist, Sarah.

> **SARAH**
>
> Robert - why did you decide
> to make a film about a
> transsexual?

> **ROBERT**
>
> My last film focused on men
> - too much, your magazine
> said - so I decided my next
> would be about femininity
> and femaleness. I wanted to
> make something more 'now'

than 'Love on the Dole' or
'The Spire', and after I saw
'The Crying Game', I realised
that transsexuals are the
most important people of the
Nineties - as we leave the
20th century behind, we're
leaving 'male' and 'female'
behind. But some things are
timeless, and I'm trying to
focus on love and sex from a
transsexual point of view.

SARAH

Are you making a 'women's
film'?

ROBERT

I wouldn't quite say that ...

SARAH

Did you have any female
inspirations?

ROBERT

I read several transsexual
memoirs - Jan Morris, April
Ashley, Christine Jorgensen
- but the one that struck
me was 'A Different Kind of
Girl' by Juliana Starr. She

was an erotic dancer and
prostitute who became the
mistress - allegedly - of a
married Tory MP, before she
died of AIDS. It's pretty
trashy and probably not
all true, but it's a good
starting point.

SARAH

It's not a well-known
book, and its publisher,
Barbarella, is no longer
running. How did you come
across it?

ROBERT

It caught my eye in a second-
hand bookshop in Soho, while
I was looking for something
else. A lucky find, I'd say.

SARAH

OK. Emily - why did you take
the part?

EMILY

I couldn't turn down the
chance to work with such
a respected director.
Once Robert told me about

Juliana's story and sent
his outline, I was sold - I
couldn't have asked for a
more challenging role.

SARAH

What does this 'challenge'
involve?

EMILY

Well, I--

ROBERT

Besides the usual difficulties
of being transsexual -
repulsed lovers, family and
friends disowning her, losing
jobs, all that - it's going
to be tough, physically.
She'll need a wig and heavy
make-up, and something extra
for the sex scenes. We've got
our technicians on that.

SARAH

I see. But not everyone
wanted to do this, did they?
Ruth McAndrew said that she
'wasn't prepared to be a
woman pretending to be a man
pretending to be a woman' and

likened it to Julie Andrews
in 'Victor/ Victoria'.
Emily - do you feel playing
this role undermines your
womanhood?

EMILY

No, I'm not my character. I read
a lot and saw just how difficult
these people's lives are - often
harder than real women.

SARAH

Don't you think transsexuals
benefit from male privilege?

EMILY

Maybe some do. But not
Juliana - she's a total
outsider.

SARAH

Emily - can you talk about
being cast opposite your
fiancé?

EMILY

We're both very excited.
It'll be totally different
to when viewers last saw us
together, in 'Passchendaele'.

ROBERT

It'll definitely give things
more spice.

EMILY

We'd better get on. Lovely
meeting you.

Emily stands and offers to shake Sarah's
hand. Sarah is more interested in checking
her dictaphone.

SARAH

Yes, you too. I'll let you
know when the piece is out
- it should be in the next
issue. Good luck with the
film.

Sarah takes her bag and exits. Emily sighs
and glances at Robert, who glares at the
door. Emily leaves, wordlessly.

FADE OUT:

FADE IN:

SCENE 2. INT. FILM STUDIO - DAY

Emily, Robert and Christian are on the set
- a Soho bedsit, curtains closed, just the
bedside lamp for light. There is a newspaper
on the bed; its triumphant headline refers to
the end of the miners' strike.

Emily wears a brown bob wig with highlights,
false eyelashes and glossy lips and a low-
cut top. Christian, in a grey suit and tie,
watches as the make-up artist unbuttons
Emily's jeans, pulls down her pants and fits a
prosthetic penis just below her waist.

> #### ROBERT
>
> Stay there - I want to see
> how that looks.
> > (He goes behind the camera)
> Hmm ... a little more light,
> please.

The assistant director shifts the reflector.

> #### EMILY
>
> It's so uncomfortable.

> #### ROBERT
>
> What is?

> #### EMILY
>
> All of it, but especially this.

>   (She pulls up her jeans)
> Why make me wear it all the
> time, just to keep strapping
> it down?

ROBERT

> So you can see what it's like
> to carry it around. Right,
> this is *big* - I want to see
> your nerves. You think he
> knows, but you don't *know* if
> he knows. You're about to find
> out, and it's terrifying.

CHRISTIAN

> Come on, there's no way he
> doesn't know. Isn't the issue
> that he can't accept it?

ROBERT

> The script says he isn't
> sure because the book says
> he wasn't sure. Perhaps he's
> been blinded by his libido.
> Sorry guys, I know it's hard,
> but it'll be worth it.

Emily and Christian look at each other,
apprehensive.

ROBERT (CONT'D)

> Right, let's try it. Sound?

ASSISTANT DIRECTOR

Sound rolling.

ROBERT

And ... action!

Emily and Christian look into each other's eyes for a moment, and then kiss. Christian grabs her breasts - she kisses him more intensely. Then he starts undoing her jeans. She tries to hold him off: he keeps going, and pulls them down, along with her pants. Then he sees her genitalia and stops, stunned.

EMILY

I thought you knew ...

CHRISTIAN

Why didn't you say?

EMILY

You didn't ask!

Christian slaps Emily and shoves her onto the bed. She gets up and swings at him, missing. He punches her. She recoils, and then grabs a pillow and hits him with it.

ROBERT

Cut! Emily, this is great, but
when he attacks you, don't
fight back so hard. Juliana is
a masochist, remember.

EMILY

Sometimes yes, but she's not
a wimp.

ROBERT

No, but she's not a prize
fighter either.

EMILY

Sorry - I'm struggling with
how passive Juliana is, a lot
of the time. Did you actually
talk to *any* transsexuals
about this?

ROBERT

Being faithful to the text
isn't enough?

EMILY

I'm not sure it is, actually.

ROBERT

The researcher has contacted
some of them. Thing is, they
barely ever let you ask them
anything.

Emily takes off the prosthetic penis and
throws it to the floor. As the assistant
director picks it up, panicked, she pulls
up her jeans, gets her coat and bag, and

walks out. Robert takes a huge mobile phone from his assistant and tries to call her. Christian stops him.

CHRISTIAN

I'll talk to her. It'll be alright.

ROBERT

It'd better be.

FADE OUT:

SCENE 3. INT. CAFE - DAY

Emily enters a café, near her home in Notting Hill. She annotates Juliana's memoir, looking at people as they come in. Kara enters, wearing black trousers, a pastel-pink blouse and sunglasses. People glance at her.

> ### EMILY
>
> You must be Kara.
>   (Offers her hand)
> I'm so happy to meet you.

> ### KARA
>
> It's an honour. I loved 'North and South'.

> ### EMILY
>
> Thanks so much for sparing the time. You were the only one who got back to me.

> ### KARA
>
> Always happy to help. But tell me - how are you approaching people?

> ### EMILY
>
> I put an advert in the *Gay Times*, and I wrote to the Beaumont Society ...

Kara puts her head in her hand, half-smiling.

                    EMILY (CONT'D)

          I also asked the Gender Clinic
          at Charing Cross if I could
          put something up there ...

                         KARA

          Darling - the *Gay Times* is
          for homosexual men. Do I look
          like a homosexual man?

Emily shakes her head.

                    KARA (CONT'D)

          And the Beaumont Society is
          for married cross-dressers -
          and their wives. The only one
          that might work is the clinic,
          but it's full of people who've
          had to talk enough about their
          'journeys' as it is.

                        EMILY

          I get that, but people bit my
          head off! Someone even said I
          was only doing this because
          it's 'trendy' ...
               (Kara turns her head.)
          I want to help!

                         KARA

          I'm grateful. Even if no-one
          else is.

EMILY

What does that mean?

KARA

I'm sorry, I'm sure you want
to help. You just don't know
the right places. Have you
got 'The Transvestite's Guide
to London'?

EMILY

I'm not looking for
transvestites.

KARA

Ah – you *have* done your
homework! It's for
transsexuals as well, or
transsexual women anyway –
we need to know where to buy
clothes and shoes too. It
lists a few venues – they're
mostly for drag queens and
cross-dressers but even if you
don't find people, you'll find
people who'll know people.

The camera pulls back, showing Kara and Emily
talking, through the window. Emily waves away
the waitress: we see her and Kara laughing
together as the scene ends.

FADE OUT:

SCENE 4. INT. EMILY AND CHRISTIAN'S HOUSE - NIGHT

Emily is dressing up - gold dress, fishnet tights, stilettos. Glittery eyeshadow, false lashes. 'The Transvestite's Guide to London' is on her desk. As she agonises over her lipstick, Christian gets home.

> **EMILY**
>
> Hi honey - how was your day?

> **CHRISTIAN (OOV)**
>
> Alright. The toothpaste ad
> only took an hour. Did you
> call Robert?

> **EMILY**
>
> Yes, it's cool. He's revising
> the script.

Christian enters and looks at Emily, who is checking her make-up. He laughs.

> **CHRISTIAN**
>
> Where are you off to?

> **EMILY**
>
> Bar Fabulous.

> **CHRISTIAN**
>
> What's that?

EMILY

It's a club for transsexuals ...
transvestites ... Whatever,
really.

CHRISTIAN

Are you going in character?

EMILY

Yes, I want to see what it's
like. Are the eyelashes too
much?

Christian hesitates.

EMILY (CONT'D)

I feel really ...

CHRISTIAN

'Inauthentic'? Here.

Christian hands Emily the wig, which was lying
on the bed. She puts on a hairnet and then
the wig, moving it obsessively. Christian
shifts it into place and smiles.

CHRISTIAN (CONT'D)

I'd kiss you, but I'd ruin
your lips.

Emily grabs Christian and kisses him.

CHRISTIAN (CONT'D)

Do you want me to come with you?

EMILY

Juliana would have gone
alone.

CHRISTIAN

Okay ... Keep safe, won't
you?

EMILY

It'll be fine. I think I pass.

CHRISTIAN

Sure, but take a taxi.
Please.

Christian gives Emily a £20 note.

EMILY

Thanks.

She pecks his cheek, gets a cardigan and
turns to leave.

CHRISTIAN

Just out of interest - what
did you put down your ...

Emily nods at the wardrobe. Christian sees
that his sock drawer is open. Emily winks,
laughs and exits.

FADE OUT:

FADE IN:

SCENE 5. EXT/INT. BAR FABULOUS - NIGHT

Emily leaves the taxi. A drag queen is on the door.

DRAG QUEEN

Evening, darling. You look
fabulous.

EMILY

Thanks.

Emily smiles and steps inside. There are
cross-dressers behind the bar, and trans women
sitting at tables, or on the dancefloor. She
sees framed pictures of Hollywood heroines
(Marilyn, Dietrich and others), a DJ booth
with a drag queen inside, and a stage with a
lamé backdrop.

She joins the queue at the bar.

1ST MAN

Hey - can I buy you a drink?

EMILY

No, I'm fine. Thanks.

She catches the barmaid's attention.

EMILY (CONT'D)

Dark rum and coke, please.

She gets out her purse.

                        1ˢᵀ MAN

Go on - let me get it.

                        EMILY

Honestly, it's alright.

                        1ˢᵀ MAN

Can I just say - you're the
most gorgeous girl I've ever
seen. So convincing.

Emily goes to the dance floor. They're playing
'Saturday Night' by Whigfield. Some trans women
are dancing around their handbags, slowly.
There are (cisgender) men, watching.

A trans woman smiles at Emily, inviting her to
join the group. She puts down her bag and tries
to relax.

                        ZELDA

You look familiar. Have we
met before?

                        EMILY

I don't think so.

                        ZELDA

Anyway, I'm Zelda.

                        EMILY

Tilda.

                        ZELDA

After Swinton?

EMILY

Haha ... yeah. Wait, are you
Zelda from--

1ˢᵀ MAN

Mind if I join you?

ZELDA

Sure.

Emily tries to continue dancing. The 1ˢᵗ Man
edges closer and puts his hand up her skirt.

1ˢᵀ MAN

Oh, you're post-op?

Emily slaps him, hard. Everyone stops: the 1ˢᵗ
Man rushes for the exit.

ZELDA

Hon, are you okay?

EMILY

I'll be alright.

Zelda takes Emily's hand and leads her towards
the toilets - the Gents' and Ladies' are next
to each other. They look in the Ladies' but
it's full, with people are doing their make-
up in the mirror, so they queue outside.

ZELDA

Darling, you been to Bar
Fabulous before?

EMILY

No, this is my first time.

ZELDA

Your voice is amazing! Who's
your coach?

EMILY

Coach? This is my real voice.

ZELDA

Oh my God, seriously? You're
so lucky. And such nice
cheekbones, too.

Emily blushes and laughs. Another man
interjects.

2ND MAN

And such kissable lips! How
about it, babe?

EMILY

How about you fuck off?

2ND MAN

Alright, I was only asking.

He walks off.

ZELDA

Tilda - you're not a
transsexual, are you?

Emily hesitates, looks around and shakes her head.

ZELDA (CONT'D)

So what made you come here?

EMILY

I was curious.

ZELDA

Sweetheart - chasers are 'curious'. You're not a chaser. So why did you come?

EMILY

Can you keep a secret?

ZELDA

Always.

EMILY

I'm an actress.

ZELDA

Of course - you're Emily Staunton! I read that interview where you said playing Juliana was a 'challenge'.

EMILY

I just meant that I knew things were hard ...

ZELDA

How did you get here tonight?

EMILY

I got a cab.

ZELDA

So you've got no idea what
it's like for us when we
have to get a bus, let alone
walk the streets. You've
got no idea what it's like
when we try to get a job,
or even go to the bathroom.
You've got no idea what it's
like when your mum slams
the phone down on you and
you know that you can never
call again, or when your
boyfriend pulls a knife on
you because he found what
you were 'hiding', even
though you were hiding
because you knew what would
happen if--

EMILY

I know it's difficult, I spoke
to people. The film deals with
sex.

ZELDA

Another tragic tranny gets
beaten and raped by some
angry john, eh?

EMILY

No, it's not like that.

ZELDA

You were going to ask if I
was Zelda from Juliana's
book, weren't you?

EMILY

Well, I--

ZELDA

Your director may be a
wanker, but he's right
when he says that her book
is bollocks. She couldn't
get her surgery on the NHS
because of her drug habit so
she needed some money to go
private, but none of the big
publishers bought it and nor
did the tabloids. Then she
found out she had AIDS and
thought she'd just scandalise
as many people as possible
before she died.

                    EMILY

Oh my God ...

                    ZELDA

And I'm sure you know, but we
don't all dress like that.

                    EMILY

Look, I want to talk more
- here's my number, get in
touch. I'll leave you alone
now. It won't be another
exploitation film, I promise.

Zelda watches Emily leave. She shakes her
head, sighs and heads back to the dancefloor.

                              FADE OUT:

SCENE 6. INT. ZELDA'S FLAT, DALSTON - EVENING

Zelda's studio flat, with a small kitchen and rickety old oven, and little fridge/freezer. There is a pan full of vegetables on the hob. The living space is a mess: books, magazines, papers and videotapes everywhere. Zelda is tidying up. There is a knock on the door - Zelda opens it to Emily and they hug.

ZELDA

Hey! Did you find it okay?

EMILY

I got a cab from Notting Hill. Thanks for taking the time, I know you're busy.

ZELDA

No problem, I wanted to talk to you.

EMILY

The food smells nice, what is it?

ZELDA

Vegetarian lasagna. One of the few good things I learned from the Hackney squats. They didn't teach me to be tidy, obviously.

EMILY

It's fine ...
    (She looks at Zelda's videos)
Jarman, Almodóvar - I love
all that.

Emily grabs a tape, 'The Death of Maria Malibran', intrigued, and then sees Zelda's 16mm Bolex camera.

EMILY (CONT'D)

Do you make films?

ZELDA

Sometimes. Just a few shorts
so far.

Emily picks up a magazine.

EMILY

Oh - you've kept our
interview ...

ZELDA

Yeah. I don't know what
Juliana would've made of it.

EMILY

You must have some idea.

ZELDA

She didn't call herself an
'outsider', I know that.
She got pretty sick of being
treated like one.

                    EMILY

         By the politicians?

Zelda laughs.

                 EMILY (CONT'D)

         What?

                    ZELDA

         Darling - I promised you the
         real story of Juliana Starr,
         didn't I?

                    EMILY

         Yes ...

                              FADE OUT:

SCENE 7. INT. HEAVEN, LONDON - EVENING

A flashback starts. Zelda is sat alone at a table at Heaven, the London gay club. 'Relax' by Frankie Goes To Hollywood is playing. Juliana, dressed in a black mesh top, pink PVC miniskirt and jacket, fishnet stockings and boots, comes over, holding a cigarette.

JULIANA

Hey babe - got a light?

Zelda gets a lighter from her bag. They smoke and talk, watching the dancefloor - there are no other women. Juliana looks at her face in a pocket mirror: she can see some five o'clock shadow. She sighs, and covers it with foundation, as Zelda gives her a reassuring rub on the shoulder.

Then there is a montage of scenes, sound-tracked by Soft Cell: Zelda and Juliana at house parties, hanging out at art galleries, taking drugs in squats. We see Zelda on the phone in a dimly lit room, talking in her sexiest voice, and Juliana talking to a cab driver on a Soho street corner.

Finally, we see them kissing and going to bed together in Juliana's bedsit.

ZELDA (V/O)

She was the first transsexual woman I ever really got to know. We didn't like the gay clubs that much, and once

we found each other, we hung
out elsewhere - squats and
communes, galleries, dive
bars, anywhere that would
have us. Gradually, we ended
up together - we didn't
really talk about it. We just
got each other.

Zelda is in their shared flat, watching a
video. Juliana enters, ashen-faced, and goes
to the bedroom.

ZELDA

Darling, what's up? Babe, I
know that look. Come on.

JULIANA

I got tested.

ZELDA

Tested? For what? Oh Jesus,
you're ... Why didn't you use
protection?

Juliana starts crying.

JULIANA

I don't think it was that.

ZELDA

I thought you were clean! Who
sold it to you?

JULIANA

Zelda, calm down--

ZELDA

If I find out who fixed you,
I'll break their fucking
neck. Was it in a squat?

JULIANA

It was with a client.

ZELDA

Fucking hell, Juliana ...
What are we gonna do?

JULIANA

I don't know.

Juliana falls onto Zelda's shoulder and weeps.

JULIANA (CONT'D)

I still had so much I wanted
to do ...

ZELDA (V/O)

So you see, Emily - it wasn't
so glamorous.

ZELDA

Why don't you write a memoir?

JULIANA

But my life's been so boring ...

ZELDA

People always say that, and
it's not true. Besides, we
can spice it up a bit.

We see Juliana's bedsit in the mid-1980s,
looking similar but not identical to Robert's
version in the mid-1990s. Rather than a
tabloid newspaper, there are posters - Laurie
Anderson and Jayne County.

JULIANA

I thought you knew ...

TORY MP

Why didn't you say?

JULIANA

You didn't ask!

As the Tory MP slaps Juliana and shoves her
onto the bed, Zelda starts talking.

ZELDA (V/O)

That never happened.

FADE OUT:

SCENE 8. INT. ZELDA'S FLAT, DALSTON - EVENING

We return to Zelda's flat. She talks over dinner. Emily looks at her, stunned.

ZELDA

> We made it all up. Partly because we hated the fucking Tories so much, given how gleeful they were that our friends all dropped dead. But mainly because we thought the tabloids would bite our hands off.

EMILY

What happened?

ZELDA

> Nobody wanted it - they didn't trust us. Rightly, I guess. Anyway - it's small fry compared to David Mellor or Stephen Milligan, perhaps they knew what was coming.

EMILY

Jesus ...

ZELDA

> Juliana died a week after she finished the manuscript. We'd hoped that we might raise

something for her funeral, but
too late. At least I got it
published. Even if no-one made
a penny. And it's full of shit.

EMILY

Well, now you can set the
record straight.

ZELDA

Nah, film people are even
worse. They'll want all that
scandal.

EMILY

Not everyone will.

ZELDA

Your director does. What's he
like?

EMILY

Well, he's got his faults. He
is kind of creepy, but he's
smart and talented, I think
we can get through to him.
Together. Look, I know you're
not sure, but the film is
going to happen-

ZELDA

Just because a book has been
optioned - if it has - doesn't
mean a movie is definitely going
to happen. And who got the
money for the rights, anyway?

EMILY

I'll introduce you to
Robert and you can ask. The
production is well underway,
I don't think you can-

ZELDA

Christ.

EMILY

I don't know how you can be
involved, but think: it could
get you off the dole, it could
get you out of this flat, it
could get you the facial surgery
you want, it could even get you
making films. Just come to the
set. I'll look after you.

ZELDA

Alright. Let's see how it
goes.

Emily gets up and approaches Zelda. They hug.

FADE OUT:

SCENE 9. INT. FILM STUDIO - DAY

Robert is talking to the Researcher as the Runner decorates the set - Juliana's bedsit. Emily enters, dramatically, with Zelda.

> ### ROBERT
>
> The prodigal child!

> ### EMILY
>
> What? You knew I was coming back.

Robert hugs Emily, for a little too long. She looks uncomfortable. Robert looks at Zelda.

> ### ROBERT
>
> And you brought a friend?

> ### EMILY
>
> Yes, this is Zelda. She's going to help.

> ### ROBERT
>
> Help?

> ### EMILY
>
> Looking at the script, making it more acc--

> ### ROBERT
>
> I told you I had the researcher on this.

EMILY

This is Zelda. From the
memoir!

Robert turns to the researcher, and glares at
him. The researcher leaves, humiliated.

ZELDA

I'd be more worried about the
book you're filming if I were
you. It's bollocks.

ROBERT

Oh yeah?

ZELDA

I co-wrote it. So yeah.

ROBERT

Why did you write a
'bollocks' book then?

ZELDA

We were skint.

ROBERT

You just gave an audience
what it wanted.

EMILY

Is that the most important
thing?

ROBERT

Wait - did no-one tell you?

EMILY

Tell me what?

Christian enters, dressed as Juliana. Emily looks at him in horror; Zelda rolls her eyes.

CHRISTIAN

I thought you were telling her!

EMILY

Telling me what?

ROBERT

Alright Christina, keep your hair on! I thought it'd make more sense if a man played the transsexual.

EMILY

It's my part!

ROBERT

You could play the wife.

EMILY

Juliana didn't have a wife!

ZELDA

Unless you mean me.

ROBERT

Clearly, it's okay to take
a bit more license. I might
try a film about a man who
breaks out of his boring life
to walk on the wild side.
It would still be your film
- you'd be trying to get him
back. And you wouldn't have
to wear the dick.

EMILY

The boring wife.
    (To Christian)
And you went along with this?

CHRISTIAN

He just said to see what it
looked like.

EMILY

Couldn't you play Zelda?

ZELDA

Couldn't *I* play Zelda?

ROBERT

You're too old to play Zelda!
I'm not sure we'll need Zelda
now, anyway.

ZELDA

Well, you can't have him as
Juliana. She never would have
worn that girly-girl top,
and what the fuck is that
posture?

ROBERT

I just said you aren't
needed.

Robert flicks his hand at the exit. Zelda
stays.

EMILY
(To Christian)
You are not doing this.

ROBERT

Then stick to the script.

ZELDA

But it's all lies!

ROBERT

Your lies!

EMILY

Why not fix them?

ROBERT

It's a feature, not a
documentary.

Emily glares at Christian. He gives her a 'not my fault' gesture. She glances at Robert and leaves; Zelda follows. Robert throws his clipboard to the floor, nearly hitting Christian.

ROBERT

Can we have one fucking shoot
that doesn't end with her
storming out?
>   (To Christian)
Don't answer that,
sweetheart. Alright, everyone
fuck off.

Robert exits. Christian stands alone for a moment, rips off his wig and goes back to the make-up room.

FADE OUT:

SCENE 10. INT. EMILY AND CHRISTIAN'S HOUSE - DAY

Emily gets home and slams the door. She hangs up her jacket and goes to the bedroom. She flings herself onto the bed. We hear gentle footsteps on the stairs. Christian stands in the doorway.

> ### CHRISTIAN
>
> Hi. I tried to call.

> ### EMILY
>
> Why didn't you follow me?

> ### CHRISTIAN
>
> In those clothes?
> (Emily closes her eyes.)
> Robert walked off. I got changed and came back. Where were you?

> ### EMILY
>
> I took Zelda for lunch. To apologise.

Christian nods.

> ### EMILY (CONT'D)
>
> You're really in with that fucking creep, aren't you?

CHRISTIAN

Look, he only said I might
try playing a transsexual in
one scene. I didn't know who
until they'd done my costume.

EMILY

'Didn't you tell her?'

CHRISTIAN

He was just covering himself.
I'd never do that to you, you
know that.

Silence. Christian sits on the bed. Emily
makes just a little room for him.

CHRISTIAN

What'll we do?

EMILY

I don't know.

CHRISTIAN

Maybe we should stick with
what we had.

EMILY

Sure, I'll give in.

CHRISTIAN

Let's meet him. Me and you.

                    EMILY

And Zelda.

                  CHRISTIAN

The main thing is that I'll
back you. If you're not the
star, I won't be either.

                    EMILY

The film needs to be honest.
That's bigger than you, and
it's bigger than me.

                  CHRISTIAN

Bigger than us. I understand.
But let's not throw
everything away. Please. I
love you.

                    EMILY

I love you too.

They kiss.

                EMILY (CONT'D)

I don't know how you'll feel
about this, but ... you
looked hot as a woman.
        (Christian laughs.)
You wanna try it?
        (He laughs again.)
Come on.

Christian undresses, nervously. Emily puts him in a bra, knickers and a dress, does his make-up and then fits the wig on him - he gradually becomes more at ease. They kiss, passionately.

                                      FADE OUT:

SCENE 11. EXT/INT. ROBERT'S OFFICE - DAY

Emily, Christian and Zelda are standing outside Robert's office, on a street in Soho. Robert turns up late.

CHRISTIAN

Hi.

ROBERT

Hello.

Robert opens the door and lets them in first, and then takes his seat behind the desk.

ROBERT (CONT'D)

I've only got three chairs.

ZELDA

I'll stand.

ROBERT

Very well. What did you decide?

CHRISTIAN

I'm not taking her part.

ROBERT

So you're sticking to the script?

EMILY

We had another idea.

ROBERT

Oh yeah?

ZELDA

We make a movie about why
Juliana and I wrote the
book we did. About life
on the dole and the game,
about transsexual clubs and
parties, about trying to
survive Thatcher and AIDS.
About how hard it is to love
and be loved in a world that
hates you.

ROBERT

It's fascinating. But
nobody's buying all that doom
and gloom any more.

CHRISTIAN

With Emily and me as
transsexual lovers?

ROBERT

Take it to Almodóvar.

ZELDA

We want you to do it.

ROBERT

I'm an auteur.

EMILY

Auteurs don't always write
their own scripts.

ROBERT

I do.

ZELDA

Do you want to make art, or
money?

ROBERT

They're not mutually
exclusive.

ZELDA

They are for you, it seems.

Zelda walks out. Emily gets up.

ROBERT

Emily, I've had enough. You
signed a contract, and it
wasn't for this.

Emily leaves, and Christian follows. Robert
lights a cigarette and stares out of the
window.

FADE OUT:

SCENE 12. EXT/INT. EMILY AND CHRISTIAN'S HOUSE - DAY

Zelda rings the bell, and looks bemused when she hears the tune - 'Ode to Joy'. Emily opens the door and hugs her. Zelda sees the family photos and twee ornaments in the hallway, and then Christian on the sofa. Zelda sits on the armchair and takes a manuscript from her bag.

> **ZELDA**
>
> So, I worked on this.

> **CHRISTIAN**
>
> You've got a script? Already?

> **ZELDA**
>
> It's just a scenario. We can work it up.

> **CHRISTIAN**
>
> 'Work it up'?

> **ZELDA**
>
> Yeah - improvise certain scenes, and work on the dialogue together.

> **EMILY**
>
> What's the plot?

ZELDA

I told you - Jules and I get
together, she gets ill, we
do the book, but it doesn't
sell. We can build your bit,
Christian, with a twist -
the memoir gets optioned for
a film, and so you have a
dilemma.

EMILY

But it's still my film?

ZELDA

Our film. So - you up for it?

CHRISTIAN

How's it going to work?

EMILY

What do you mean?

CHRISTIAN

Well - who's paying for it?

ZELDA

It won't cost much, but I'll
need your help - finding a
crew, and some funding. But
I'll shoot on VHS. It's cheap
but it looks beautiful, and
it'll fit the Eighties vibe.

CHRISTIAN

And you'll direct?

ZELDA

Yeah.

CHRISTIAN

Look ... I don't know.

EMILY

Let's try a few scenes. You did for Robert.

ZELDA

I need both of you if it's going to work.

CHRISTIAN

Where will we shoot?

ZELDA

We'll make a calling card scene at my place. It's where Juliana lived, so it's already one up on Robert.

CHRISTIAN

And what about Robert?

EMILY

I can't work with him.

CHRISTIAN

You might have to, darling.

EMILY

If he likes what we do, maybe
we can work something out.

CHRISTIAN

I doubt it. But ... let's
see.

Zelda hugs Christian. He lets go and kisses
Emily.

FADE OUT:

FADE IN:

SCENE 13. INT. ZELDA'S FLAT - DAY

Emily is dressed as Juliana, and Christian as Zelda. The actual Zelda is directing, holding a VHS camera.

> **ZELDA**
>
> Right, here I'm apologising to Juliana for blaming her for getting ill. She doesn't reply so I suggest the book.

> **EMILY**
>
> Is that how it was?

> **ZELDA**
>
> Close enough. Okay, go on the bed ...

Emily and Christian sit. Zelda moves with the camera.

> **ZELDA (CONT'D)**
>
> I'll have to shoot from the bathroom, it's the only way I'll get the right distance.

> **EMILY**
>
> How will you cut it?

ZELDA

We'll do it from a few
angles. I might try some
double exposures too.

CHRISTIAN

Good luck getting people to
fund it with tricks like
that.

ZELDA

We'll do a straight-up love
scene, that'll reel them in.
Well, maybe not 'straight'.

EMILY

What do we do?

ZELDA

Just kiss. Then heat it up.

Emily and Christian kiss. They caress each
other, and Emily starts to remove Christian's
top.

ZELDA

Okay - guys, this is great,
but Christian, you need to
lead.

CHRISTIAN

You were the domme?

ZELDA

I'll show you.

CHRISTIAN

No, it's fine, I get it.

ZELDA

Go on then.

Christian kisses Emily, and then gets her into bed. He puts his hand down her top and touches her chest.

ZELDA

Cut!

Zelda puts one hand on Christian's head, the other on his bust. Christian leans into Zelda - she kisses him, and they make out, passionately.

EMILY

Do you want my part?

ZELDA

I'm just showing him what to do.

EMILY

'Just showing him'?

CHRISTIAN

Sorry.

Zelda goes to the toilet. Emily glares at Christian.

                    CHRISTIAN (CONT'D)

          I just like the clothes,
          that's all. Please don't tell
          anyone.

                         EMILY

          Why didn't you tell me?

                       CHRISTIAN

          I thought you'd leave ... I
          worried you'd tell people...

                         EMILY

          Darling, I'd never do that to
          you.

Zelda returns.

                         ZELDA

          Let's try it again. On film -
          tape - I think you've got it.

Christian kisses Emily, and then gets her into bed. He puts his hand down her top and touches her chest.

                    ZELDA (CONT'D)

          Wonderful! Let's try again
          from over here.

Zelda moves in. Christian and Emily repeat the scene.

ZELDA (CONT'D)

Cut! That's even better.

EMILY

It feels great.

CHRISTIAN

Shall we go on, or take it
back to Robert?

EMILY

Let's decide when we've got a
few scenes.

ZELDA

That's enough for today,
anyway. We'll get back
together on Friday.

Christian goes to the toilet.

ZELDA (CONT'D)

Do you need help getting your
make-up off?

EMILY

He can manage. Trust me.
(Whispers) Look, I know we're
doing an amateur film now, but
can you keep it professional?

ZELDA

Sorry ... I didn't think it'd
be this weird.

EMILY

Do you fancy him? When he's
you, I mean?

ZELDA

It's just ... you seem so
happy together ...

EMILY

You're trying to break us up?

ZELDA

No, of course not! It's so
hard not to think about how
life could've been ...

EMILY

Normal?

ZELDA

Better ...

Zelda starts crying. Emily sits her on the
sofa and puts her arm around her. Christian
comes back and nods at Zelda; Emily gestures
to say, 'She'll be fine'.

FADE OUT:

FADE IN:

SCENE 14. INT. ROBERT'S OFFICE - DAY

Robert is at his desk, with Christian, Emily and Zelda. There is a VCR and TV on a trolley in a corner - Zelda holds a videotape.

ROBERT

Right, what have you got?

EMILY

We'll show you.

Zelda plays the tape. The scene plays out. It's tinted blue rather than in colour, with various double exposures laying scenes from Zelda's past over Juliana telling Zelda about her HIV test and the reconciliation. Ambient music plays over the make-up sex. Robert looks sceptical during the HIV scenes and bored when archive footage of trans women at a Pride march appears, but excited about the sex scenes. Zelda and Emily notice him smiling, and exchange a small grin.

ROBERT

It's interesting. How are you funding it?

CHRISTIAN

We're struggling.

ROBERT

I'll bet. Nobody wants this
sub-Warhol shit. Let alone
all this prattle about class.
It might be set ten years ago
but it's not the Eighties
now, is it?

CHRISTIAN

I have to say - I don't like
the flag-waving either.

EMILY

It doesn't *look* like an
Eighties film.

ROBERT

You weren't at film school
then, were you? Count
yourself lucky: I had to sit
through some absolute dreck.
     (To Zelda)
You let the rights to this
book go into the public
domain, didn't you?

Christian and Emily turn to Zelda.

ROBERT (CONT'D)

Nobody has signed anything.

ZELDA

We couldn't marry, even if
we'd wanted to - obviously
- and Juliana's family had
long since lost touch. We
didn't expect much so I told
the publisher to donate any
royalties to the Terrence
Higgins Trust and to reserve
the rights. But we'd be
making a film *about* the book,
not *of* it.

ROBERT

I can see what my legal team
make of that.
    (He turns to Emily and Christian)
Either way, you two signed up
with me. So, what'll it be?

EMILY

I've had enough.

ROBERT

You're not the only one.
Christian? If you do this
film, my way, then I'll let
Emily out of her contract.
Final offer.

Emily looks at Christian. Zelda gets her tape and exits, holding back tears. Emily takes Christian's hand and stares into his eyes, not seeing Robert glare at them.

FADE OUT:

SCENE 15. INT. ROBERT'S OFFICE - DAY

Robert is at his desk, reading a letter.

> **CHRISTIAN (V/O)**
>
> Dear Robert,
>
> I am writing to apologise,
> and because I think it is
> best that we have everything
> on paper. I am afraid that I
> cannot continue with the film.
> I should have said so when we
> last met with Emily.

FADE OUT:

SCENE 16. INT. CHRISTIAN AND EMILY'S HOUSE - DAY

Emily and Christian are having a blazing row: she is screaming at him.

EMILY

A promise from you is worth fuck all!

Emily throws a cushion at Christian and storms out. The screen goes black, and Christian's V/O covers the transition to the next scene.

CHRISTIAN (V/O)

I am trying to persuade her not to give up on her dream, or on me. Maybe I can bring her back to acting, at least. I'm not hopeful, and - as I'm sure you understand - this has been why my performances as Juliana haven't worked out.

FADE OUT:

SCENE 17. INT. FILM STUDIO - DAY

We see Christian on set as Juliana, kissing the politician, played by another man. It's strangely lifeless, and in a close-up we see Christian looking stilted, awkward. Angry, Robert cuts.

FADE OUT:

SCENE 18. INT. ROBERT'S OFFICE - DAY

CHRISTIAN (V/O)

I know you will be unhappy
with the outcome, but in
the long term, I think it's
best for all of us. I hope
that we can find an agreement
regarding our contracts, and
that you find another way to
make this film.

Yours,

Christian.

Robert puts the letter in a drawer and exits.

FADE OUT:

SCENE 19. EXT. CINEMA - EVENING

CAPTION: 'TWO YEARS LATER'

Robert is attending a film premiere. He looks
aged: he's lost some hair and grown stubble,
wearing sunglasses. Beautiful people enter
the cinema as cameras flash. A journalist
thrusts a microphone towards his face.

JOURNALIST

Robert - tell us about your
new film.

ROBERT

This is a passion project.
I've always loved Orwell, and
'A Clergyman's Daughter' has
been unfairly ignored. I was
happy to get such good people
involved, they were so easy
to work with.

JOURNALIST

This is a surprise, isn't it,
given that many people were
expecting your transsexual
film with Christian Brady and
Emily Staunton? Can you tell
us what's happened to that?

                    ROBERT

          They weren't right for the
          script, and then I felt the
          time was right to do this. I
          might still go back to it.
          Thanks.

Robert shoves past the journalist, who looks
bemused, and goes inside.

                              FADE OUT:

SCENE 20 (EPILOGUE). INT/EXT. VARIOUS LOCATIONS - DAY

The screen goes blue.

ZELDA (V/O)

'A Clergyman's Daughter'
was critically acclaimed,
but then Robert made more
commercial films. You've
probably seen some of them.

Clip from Robert's 'The True Story of the People's Princess' (2004), showing Diana and Dodi Fayed together by a swimming pool.

ZELDA (V/O) (CONT'D)

Christian stayed in film, but
he wasn't so lucky.

Clip of Christian playing a butler, with just a little dialogue, in 'Rhodes to Freedom', a British film about Cecil Rhodes made in 2001, and already forgotten.

ZELDA (V/O) (CONT'D)

He came out as a cross-
dresser in 2012 and got a
couple of bit-parts off the
back of this.

Clip of Christian playing an older transvestite in a Channel 4 drama.

> **ZELDA (V/O) (CONT'D)**
> Disillusioned, Emily quit
> acting, left London and took
> up teaching.

Shot of Emily teaching English in a secondary school, in what looks like a white, middle-class area. Both her and the children look bored and frustrated.

FADE OUT:

SCENE 21 (EPILOGUE). INT. ZELDA'S FLAT, DALSTON - DAY

Shot of Zelda in the present, at her desk. She's still in the same flat, but it's cleaner and tidier.

ZELDA (V/O)

And me? Well - I've written this film. It felt like the only way to set things straight. I hoped you liked it.

FADE OUT:

THE END

CROSSING

The three people interviewed here were all part of a trans/queer performance art and activist group in Brighton in the late 2000s, when the prevalence of a mainstream LGBT culture fuelled by the 'Pink Pound' and (particularly) the commodification of Pride led a number of individuals – especially trans, genderqueer and non-binary people – to seek a new community and try to create a more radical counter-culture. Although the collective discussed here was short-lived, we feel that the events described below should be included in this oral history of Brighton & Hove's LGBT community, and hope similar organisations may learn from them.

NB: We have added explanations of certain venues, events and terms that will doubtless be familiar to locals, but perhaps not to anyone in a different time or place. The pronouns used for (and by) each interviewee are the ones they specified.

Sarah Jarrett

Editor, Speaking Out: An Oral History of LGBT People in Brighton & Hove (Old Steine Books, 2012)

....

'I thought I could find a safe space in Brighton's queer scene after so many years of passing, crossing, wandering. Away from misogyny in parts of the British Asian community, racism in British Caucasian circles, and the transphobia everywhere. But it turned out to be anything but: people not bothering to say hello to me, either because I was brown, or because I was a femme trans woman who was into men, and that was counter-revolutionary.'

– Sabina Tharkur, 'Crossing' *(Written for a performance at the West Hill Community Hall in 2009 and published at her blog,* Brown and Out in Brighton and London, *in August 2011.)*

MILITANCIJA: I'll let you decide whose fault it was. I shouldn't keep having to pick sides.

SABINA THARKUR: I reckon Venus will still blame me for being uppity.

VENUS N. FURZ: Sabina could have sorted it all out, any time she liked.

SABINA: Told you.

VENUS: I'm not sure if the group could have held together for long, anyway.

MILITANCIJA: Too many egos.

SABINA: Just one, I'd say. But sometimes that's all it takes.

MILITANCIJA: It started so well! I put on a queer disco at the Cowley Club on London Road. I was DJ-ing with a couple of friends, playing The Gossip, Peaches, Jeffree Star. We got a good crowd, and a few people said they'd like to come to more nights like this. Maybe something where they could perform, as well as dance.

VENUS: I'd been going to London, seeing this guy I met in Shoreditch. We went to loads of clubs – Duckie, Trannyshack, Bar Wotever. I saw these phenomenal drag queens at the Royal Vauxhall Tavern who came on as a mistress and a slave – the mistress was dressed up like Rebekah Brooks, and the slave was one of her readers, put in bondage and made to read *Sun* headlines, *Clockwork Orange*-style, being whipped whenever she said that not all Muslims were terrorists or that transsexual people should be allowed surgery on the NHS. By the end, quoting an old *Sun* editorial about Brighton being 'a nasty town of drugs, gays, AIDS and drunks', she admitted: perverts *had* to be wiped out, and only the Tories and the Church 'could save our souls!' It was so refreshing to be in a room full of people who felt like I did. And it was as funny as fuck.

MILITANCIJA: I'd been in Brighton for four years, and we'd never had a space for anything like that. If you were lucky, you got one of the old drag acts at the Queen's Arms, or the Harlequin, but even that had closed down. Otherwise it was just the bars around the pier, full of straights and twinks. So, I started looking for venues where we could do something regular ...

VENUS: ... And I was looking for acts who might perform. I loved Jonny Woo and Ma Butcher at Gay Bingo, and Pia's horror-dance, *O Superman*, at Horse Meat Disco, where she came on as this weird Clark Kent in a rubber-doll mask and kept stripping – first down to a Superman costume, then a muscleman, and finally a trans woman, with loads of fake blood to reveal that deep down, we were all just guts. That was cool. I liked Michael Twaits' post-drag poem about Stonewall, too – this hot mess in a blonde wig and black dress, beautiful but never trying to 'pass', talking about a 'normal night' where 'you could fuck anyone'. S/he made me feel like I was *in* the queer underground, hanging out with Candy Darling or something. I got more involved, and after I dressed up in a corset, a maid's outfit with 'Not Your Slave' on the tabard in red lipstick, and four inch' heels and ran the 100m at the Tranny Olympics, I knew I'd found my calling. In the queer scene, that is, not as an athlete – it took me a few minutes to reach the end. Anyway, I couldn't afford to move to London – even before the credit crunch – but we could build something at home.

SABINA: The London scene was diverse to a point, but like Brighton: lots of nationalities, but still pretty white. But I went to the final Transfabulous festival that summer *(2008)* in London and Ignacio Rivera's act blew my mind. It was all about a butch dyke, trying to get out of Hawaii by dancing for tourists for money. All this stuff about being a girl who wants to be a boy, pretending to be a girly girl to pay for hormones and surgery, all the genders you could choose … But Rivera never forgot about being a QTIPOC *(queer, trans and/or intersex person of colour)*. Nobody had told me you could be Bengali, trans and queer – let alone all these things, *and* a fabulous artist.

MILITANCIJA: We liked how Transfabulous responded to the Gender Recognition Act (2004), which only acknowledged people who defined as 'male' or 'female', with the Festival making space for those who wouldn't (or couldn't) tick one of those boxes to explore their identities creatively. We formed a committee, with a few others we'd met around town, or through queer mailing lists, and organised a fundraiser called 'Recognise Me?' at the West Hill Community Hall. I'd play some tunes, then we'd show a few short films and introduce a couple of local performers, both of whom I'd met through the Cowley Club: Sabina and Venus.

SABINA: I designed a poster with the name of the night and the group – after we voted to call ourselves 'NuQueer Power'. Venus's idea. I modelled my drawing on Zanele Muholi's photos of black queers people in South Africa. Venus said it was 'too political'. I guess they meant 'the wrong kind of political'. I re-did it without the image and got the committee's approval ...

VENUS: ... And I put them round the gay bars in Kemp Town, took some to the London clubs, posted about it on the forums, got it in the listings for the free Brighton LGBT publications, *GScene* and *3Sixty,* and told my mates.

MILITANCIJA: Soon, we were ready to launch. I was so excited!

VENUS: We agreed to show the films first, before Sabina's performance. I would headline and then Mili would DJ.

MILITANCIJA: Everyone loved the films. We had a ten-minute documentary about an Austrian performer called Lucy McEvil, one of Maria Beatty's fetish films, and *Bilocation,* a short piece by two lesbian artists from Slovenia – Marina Gržinić & Aina Šmid.

VENUS: Then Sabina went on.

SABINA: Of course, I worried that my piece might not go down well. You always do, whenever you perform anything, wherever you do it. But I'd given it a lot of thought, and trusted everyone in the room to engage with it, at least.

Militancija: Sabina and I had spoken about it. I thought it'd be cool.

Venus: Militancija never read the script. Sabina didn't even bother to mention it to me.

Sabina: I came on dressed in a red bordered sari and bindi, to a soundtrack by Nishat Khan, and asked the audience who they saw. An English woman? A European transsexual? An Asian transgender person? Indian, Pakistani, Bangladeshi? The music stopped, and I spoke about how my parents had moved to England in the Seventies – Birmingham, then Leicester – so my father could study medicine. I told them about the racist abuse they got, not long after the Tory MP in Birmingham campaigned on that slogan that used the N-word to ask people about who they might want as their neighbours, and won. I talked about how my mother worked in a primary school, and was popular with her pupils until parents started saying they didn't want 'one of them' teaching their children.

Militancija: The crowd had a lot of empathy.

Sabina: I talked about how I was born in Leicester in the early Eighties, the effects of Thatcher, and how my mother was the first to get laid off when the education budget got slashed – the usual divide-and-rule tactics that my parents' Irish friends often mentioned. I rubbed off my bindi and took off the sari – underneath, I was wearing a Leicester City football shirt, jeans and trainers, like I had when I hung out with the guys from school. In place of Nishat Khan, I put on

The Smiths – my favourite band as a teenager. I liked them more than the Britpop the white kids were into: Oasis or Blur, all that flag-waving. The Smiths were all about feeling like an outsider, and yet I was listening to them in my attempt to fit in. After all, they still played guitar like the straight lads, and they were still white … And just as Morrissey sang, *You shut your mouth, how can you say I go about things the wrong way*, I cut the music.

Venus: It was very moving.

Sabina: And went into *Bengali in Platforms,* from Morrissey's first solo album. That feeling when I found the tape at a charity shop, saw the title (*Viva Hate*) and thought, 'He *gets* me.' Then I put the cassette on and heard him sing *Shelve your Western plans and understand / That life is hard enough when you belong here* – implying that I didn't.

Militancija: Lots of people weren't comfortable – Morrissey was a hero to them.

Sabina: The soundtrack changed – *Ten Ragas to a Disco Beat* by Charanjit Singh, a mixture of Western dance, often appropriated by white people from black communities, and traditional Indian music. I discussed how I tried to embrace my dualities, rather than becoming obsessed with integrating – 'passing' – as the politicians, Labour or Tory, as well as the tabloids and the people around me demanded. The challenges of living as a woman. I put the sari on again and recounted some abuse that had been thrown at me: racist, sexist, transphobic. The audience felt divided when

I said how 'tranny' had been used as an insult – there were arguments about whether 'we' should try to 'reclaim' it – but they did at least wince when they heard the P-word, like they did when I mentioned that racist election slogan from the mid-Sixties, safely in the past … After the silence, I recalled trying to find a space that felt right, embracing bits of British culture I liked while remembering where my family were from.

VENUS: If she'd stopped there, it would've been fine.

SABINA: I took off the sari again, stood on stage in just a bra and undies, vulnerable. There was silence as I draped myself in a Union Jack – Morrissey-style. I talked about how people in the UK knew nothing about Ireland, let alone India. I told them about how my great-grandfather was one of a thousand shot dead by British soldiers in the Amritsar massacre of 1919, and how my grandparents were uprooted by the rioting caused by the partition in 1947, as Muslims in India and Hindus in Pakistan had to flee their homes. I talked about how millions of tons of wheat were exported from India to Britain while we died of starvation – up to three million Bengalis lost their lives in 1943 alone, when Winston Churchill said he hated Indians, 'a beastly people with a beastly religion', and that the famine was our fault 'for breeding like rabbits'.

MILITANCIJA: You could feel the shock in the crowd. They probably weren't the kind who loved Churchill, but they were nearly all British, and conditioned to see him as a hero. Sabina cut through years of that.

SABINA: I dropped the flag. Near-naked, I talked about how white Brits had no idea about any of this. Instead, they'd tell me how good the Empire was for India, even though India was one of the world's richest countries in 1750 and one of the poorest by 1950. I talked about how white people kept saying the British gifted us railways – ignorant of the fact that they were paid for by Indian taxes, for the East India Company to move stolen resources, without a care for how much they cost 'the natives' – who, of course, weren't allowed to work on the trains, even if white-only carriages were soon ditched for economic reasons. I said that not only was this never taught in schools, but white people never even *tried* to educate themselves about it.

MILITANCIJA: The tension in the room was tangible.

VENUS: It wasn't supposed to be a lecture.

SABINA: I put *Bengali in Platforms* back on, and talked about trying to find a safe space in the Brighton queer scene. Away from the misogyny I'd encountered in parts of the British Asian community, the racism in British Caucasian circles, and the transphobia I'd experienced everywhere. But it had proved to be anything but: people not bothering to say hello to me, either because I was brown, or because I was a femme trans woman who was into men, and that was counter-revolutionary. People parroting the same ignorant clichés to me about the benefits of Empire, or asking where I was 'really' from, seeing India, Pakistan and Bangladesh as one big colony. Telling me I was 'always bringing up racism' and that they had always opposed it 'by telling people not to say the N-word', but never going any further – never reading books or watching films by brown or Black people, always making us do the emotional labour of 'proving' that something was racist. I ended by reminding the audience that as an artist, my role was to ask questions. It was their responsibility to work out the answers.

VENUS: I thought she'd leave the stage with a mic drop.

MILITANCIJA: I yelled, 'Let's give it up for Sabina Tharkur!' A couple of people clapped.

VENUS: They'd come to feel supported, not hectored.

MILITANCIJA: I tried again, but didn't get much more of a response. I carried on. 'Please give a big welcome to our headline act, Venus N. Furz!'

VENUS: How was I meant to follow that?

SABINA: Venus had plenty of friends there. People whistled when they came on, at least.

VENUS: I did my best to change the mood. My piece was called 'Nancy Boy'. I tied my hair in bunches, plastered my face in purple eyeshadow and my beard in glitter, wore a sequinned silver dress with 'tranny' daubed across it in lipstick, ripped fishnets with neon-pink heels. I ran on to the Placebo song, joining in with Brian Molko on 'Comes across all shy and coy / Just another nancy boy.' I'd done that in rehearsal; the idea of me being shy and coy had got a big laugh. On the night? Sweet FA. Just as Molko got to *Different partner / every night*, I yelled 'Hang on!' I stopped the track and pointed at the speakers:

'Is he trying to say that I'm a slag?'

Pockets of laughter – nothing more. I'm a professional, so I soldiered on. I talked about how I'd fallen into 'the trap of passing', struggling to look like a six foot woman, looking like a lanky bloke looking like a giant woman trying not to look like a tall man. I held my head back and gulped, as if worried about getting the shit kicked out of me, but I was just making an exhibition of my Adam's apple.

I repeated bits of Agrado's monologue in Pedro Almodóvar's *All about My Mother* about doing sex work to pay for cosmetic surgery, so she became more authentic. 'I didn't have money or time for that,' I said. 'I was too busy being *me*. *Becoming* me.'

'Through endless sex – frantic, tantric, not always fantastic but sometimes ecstatic – I let the boys find the girl in me, and this beautiful butterfly began to emerge, spreading its incandescent wings. My body is the sword and my identity is the pen: mighty, fighting, finally uniting, I'm a proud gender outlaw, planning a *coup d'état* to establish the Dictatorship of the Divine.' When I did that at Trannyshack the year before, there were cheers – actual cheers – and I was told London crowds were hard to please!

By now, it was obvious – this wasn't going to work. Every self-effacing quip got taken literally; every gag bombed through the floor. I tried to expand on different experiences: blokes on websites for 'T-girls and their admirers' who told me they were wanking over my photos in their wives' knickers, or asking me to dress them like babies and spank them until they cried; men who'd gone to bed with me for the first time and puked, like in *The Crying Game* or *Ace Ventura*; guys who'd tell me they were crazy *about* me one moment, then went crazy *at* me the next. I put *Nancy Boy* back on – I'd cut it up a bit – and on the line, 'It all breaks down at the role reversal,' I took off my wig and dress and confronted the audience with my maleness – my manhood. Even *that* didn't get a rise. Sorry – no pun intended, honestly …

'Here I am,' I said. 'Finally coming home – coming out – to my people.' Again, not a peep. I put the dress back on, snatched the wig and walked offstage.

MILITANCIJA: I tried to get a party started with *Fuck the Pain Away* by Peaches.

VENUS: You might as well have played the bloody *Funeral March*.

SABINA: The look Venus gave me as they came off stage was unreal – I hadn't seen that since my last Anti-Nazi League demo in Leicester. I went backstage (to the kitchen) and asked Venus if they were alright. I just got told I 'shouldn't have spoiled the vibe like that'. I wondered what they meant – apparently it 'wasn't that kind of party'. I replied, 'What kind of party *is* it then?' Not a word.

MILITANCIJA: I left my friend Olga in charge of the decks and went to check on Venus and Sabina. I caught Venus walking out and told them we'd discuss it all at our next meeting. Venus went 'Yeah, whatever,' and left. Sabina seemed quite shaken: I had to go back to the booth, but I hugged her and said we'd go to the meeting together. I texted Venus, but no reply.

SABINA: I felt like Venus should do their own reading about queer scenes and race. They were always going on about *Nobody Passes* by Mattilda Bernstein Sycamore, so I thought they had.

MILITANCIJA: They did show up to that next organising meeting, at least.

SABINA: And immediately assumed they'd be the chair.

VENUS: It was my turn. We'd agreed that the last time.

SABINA: Venus didn't think it appropriate to stand down.

VENUS: Why should I?

MILITANCIJA: After a long argument, it was decided – by a single vote – that I'd take over.

SABINA: The first thing Venus did was ask if one vote was sufficient.

VENUS: Get someone who calls hirself 'Militancija' to resolve a conflict. *Genius*.

MILITANCIJA: I managed to keep them both at the table. They sat glaring at each other.

SABINA: Me on one side; Venus and their mates on the other.

MILITANCIJA: I had to start with a review of Saturday's event.

VENUS: Everyone sighed.

SABINA: Not enough back slapping.

VENUS: All I said was that Sabina's piece might have scared some people off. Then I suggested we agree all performances before the events. Not the scripts – just the general content.

MILITANCIJA: I said we shouldn't make anyone justify themselves.

SABINA: But that's what happened. I said it was a Stalinist nightmare.

VENUS: Which was an over-reaction. Anyway, Sabina had defenders.

SABINA: One person, who wasn't scared of Venus's gang.

MILITANCIJA: Who said her performance *was* exactly what we should be doing, and that we shouldn't compromise our spontaneity.

VENUS: But that was no good if people stopped coming. As my friend, Julie Binder, asked – what about our safe space policy?

SABINA: That was meant to protect people of colour, not shut them down.

MILITANCIJA: By this time, the meeting was hopelessly split. I was hammering the table with my fist and telling everyone to calm down.

VENUS: I told Sabina that wasn't fair. I'd been to anti-BNP *(British National Party)* demos, and some of my friends supported the Anti-Nazi League.

SABINA: Which just made it worse that they wouldn't listen to me. I thought about it for a moment, but decided not to say that Venus had never mentioned anything about Antifa to me before, even when I'd talked about going to Barking to protest against the BNP in 2006. Instead, I asked Venus and friends to reflect on who gets to speak, and on which terms. Then, I told them more about racism and trans-misogyny I'd experienced in the queer scene. If they'd read *Whipping Girl* by Julia Serano about 'Sexism and the Scapegoating of Femininity', I said, they might recognise it. I mentioned how I was told the first queer night at the Cowley was run by AFAB people *for* AFAB people, and that someone on the door had told me to wear a longer skirt. Then I explained how more than one person on the dancefloor thought it was fine to shove their hands up my dress, just because I was trans. They all said they'd never seen any of that.

VENUS: We weren't saying it didn't happen. Just that we didn't know about it.

MILITANCIJA: I suggested we focus on the future – how we could make the space safer for everyone. But Sabina took it as silencing, and I realised it was the wrong thing to say.

SABINA: Unlike some, Militancija apologised straight away. I said I'd still like to perform, even if I wasn't comfortable with having to discuss the contents up front.

VENUS: 'Fine', I replied, 'but I'm not sure I want to perform with you.'

MILITANCIJA: I tried to remain impartial, but by now it was impossible.

VENUS: Bollocks, s/he took Sabina's side.

SABINA: S/he just reiterated that no-one should be barred from performing.

VENUS: *No-one?* What if one of the BNP's LGBT branch wanted to do a set?

MILITANCIJA: 'Don't be ridiculous', I said.

SABINA: So then Venus and their mates accused Militancija and me of silencing *them*.

VENUS: You were!

MILITANCIJA: I made another error, making the first one worse. I suggested a vote.

SABINA: You know that saying 'scratch a liberal, find a Tory'? Sometimes you scratch a radical and find a liberal.

MILITANCIJA: I said sorry. Again. We ended with no resolution, and no second date.

VENUS: I walked out.

SABINA: Me too.

MILITANCIJA: Really, that was the end of the group.

VENUS: No-one ever said so, though.

SABINA: I started looking for other places to hang out. But that's the trouble with a town this size – it's big enough to have a lot of different scenes, but only one of each, so if you fall out with a scene, or it collapses, or it's just not for you, that's it. I tried some of the bars near the sea front, but they were for white gay guys, who didn't want to talk to me, except to take the piss out of my clothes, or occasionally hit on me and then laugh about it. Anyway, I found them quite old school, even though they were new, and pretty dull.

MILITANCIJA: One night I was walking back to my little flat on Montague Street, and bumped into Sabina. We hadn't seen each other since that meeting, and she looked lonely.

SABINA: I felt alienated from everyone and wanted to move. Maybe London, maybe Kolkata. But I was skint.

MILITANCIJA: At first she didn't want to talk, but I said I wanted to be friends and offered her a drink. I realised I'd have to apologise – she was more gracious than I might have been.

SABINA: Mili suggested we start our own night. But where? And with whom?

MILITANCIJA: We decided to try the Marlborough Theatre on Princes Street. It had been my favourite hang-out when I first came here from Split, playing pool with the local lesbians who loved having a baby dyke.

SABINA: Mili spoke to a friend there, and we got a date. We'd still have to promote it through all the usual venues, though, including the ones I'd finished with. We got to the Cowley to find Venus had left flyers for the next 'NuQueer Power' night at the West Hill Hall – which we knew nothing about, and which they were headlining, obviously.

MILITANCIJA: Same date that we'd planned. Sabina was furious.

SABINA: Fucking right I was! They had no right to do that.

MILITANCIJA: I tried to get her to calm down – the barman at the Cowley was looking at us, and if I hadn't taken Sabina outside, he might have asked us to leave, which would've made everything worse. She was shaking but there was nowhere for her emotion to go. I said we should react with something positive. The Brighton Fringe Festival was coming up – I suggested she expand her piece into a solo show. I'd DJ and compere.

SABINA: It sounded good. I'd co-organise it with Queers Against Racism.

MILITANCIJA: We secured a slot at the Marly – changing it to the night after Venus's gig. We decided to go to their show at the West Hill Hall, and hand out our flyers there.

SABINA: We got there just after the start time. I don't know who was on the door, but it wasn't anyone from the committee, so we got straight in.

MILITANCIJA: We hung out at the back, watching Venus lap up all the praise from their mates.

SABINA: We wondered if they'd boot us out, but they were too self-absorbed, as ever.

MILITANCIJA: I hardly recognised anyone. I thought I knew all the queers in Brighton.

SABINA: No people of colour, surprisingly. Eventually, I did see a few familiars – they shot me a few swift, disapproving glances, but no more than that.

MILITANCIJA: 'I've got your back,' I assured her.

SABINA: When Venus came on to introduce the first performer, I held up a Queers Against Racism placard.

MILITANCIJA: Not popular. But necessary.

SABINA: At first, they just tried to ignore it. But then a commotion rose up in the crowd.

VENUS: I carried on.

MILITANCIJA: Someone yelled, 'Our shows call out racism!'

SABINA: Then: 'You just hate white people!'

VENUS: I told the crowd to calm down – everyone was there to have a good time.

MILITANCIJA: The first performer was one of Venus's friends, Victor/Victorious, who'd been at the Cowley Club meeting. The usual stuff about sometimes hiding your chest, other times wearing a bra, sometimes being a man, sometimes a woman.

SABINA: If you'd never been to any queer nights in London, it might've been a revelation. To be fair, some of the younger people hadn't.

VENUS: I came back to introduce the second act – Radclyffe Hell.

MILITANCIJA: I thought it might be alright – a swipe at reality television.

SABINA: A white person's anti-racist show. Probably at Venus's insistence.

VENUS: It was going to deal with the scandal on *Celebrity Big Brother*, but Jade Goody – one of the people who'd said racist (and transphobic) insults to Indian actress Shilpa Shetty, saying Shetty had 'a big hairy face' and 'looked like a man' and taking the piss out of her accent – died just before we did the gig, so Radclyffe had to rethink.

MILITANCIJA: Radclyffe announced that s/he'd dressed as Davina McCall, who used to host those shows.

VENUS: Inspired by that drag show I'd seen at the RVT, Victor and I played The Audience. Vic said it was fun to dress up like a typical 'chav' – can of Stella, Adidas trackie bottoms and football T-shirt, Brylcreem hair – and for me to be his bird, in hoop earrings, pink crop top and jeans, diamanté stilettos. Riotous laughter.

MILITANCIJA: Sabina murmured to me: 'So fucking radical, having a stab at the povvos.'

SABINA: I couldn't be arsed with a more thoughtful critique. They didn't *know* that working class communities had always contained anti-racist elements along with the racist ones, as well as some brown and Black people, because they didn't *know* any working-class people. So I just booed. It was quite cathartic.

VENUS: I should've known *someone* would object to it.

MILITANCIJA: Nobody joined us. The atmosphere strained further with each line of their show.

VENUS: Sabina and Mili wouldn't give us a chance, but we were building towards a twist. Radclyffe – Davina – was trying to apologise to the 'viewers at home' about 'the kind of vile abuse that we never could have anticipated when we locked a bunch of people with reputations for being unpleasant into a house and broadcast it for a nation full of insecure, beer-chugging nobodies to knock them off their pedestals'. But halfway through the sentence, Mili yelled, 'Bougie bullshit!'

MILITANCIJA: Seriously, even David fucking Cameron wouldn't have said something like that. Not when he was still pretending not to be posh, anyway.

VENUS: Everyone told hir to shut up. Correctly.

SABINA: Actually, a few people laughed. Correctly.

VENUS: They laughed because the next thing that happened was that Victor and me – The Masses – reached through the TV screen and kidnapped Davina. We tied her up, S&M style, with a ball gag and handcuffs, and made her sit on the couch, while we stepped into the frame and replaced her in the world of celebrity. We winked at the audience and said, 'Wouldn't you like to see *this* on the telly?' Then we stripped down to our underwear and made out.

SABINA: Proles! Shed the trappings of your class and your identity! Then you may be liberated!

VENUS: Oh, for fuck's sake.

MILITANCIJA: They got a dizzying reception – whistling, whooping, the works.

SABINA: They kept smooching until the applause finally died down. Then Venus came on and took a bow, lapping it up before yelling, 'Now it's time for the star of the show ...'

MILITANCIJA: Venus's friends practically waved their clapping hands under my nose.

SABINA: Venus's act was about 'wreckers' in the queer scene – 'enemies of free speech'.

VENUS: No, it was about unity.

SABINA: 'Enemies of free speech'?

VENUS: That was ironic. Anyway – no different from you calling us Stalinists, is it?

SABINA: As you said on stage.

VENUS: What made you do this interview with me, anyway?

SABINA: The people from the Oral History Project told me you'd agreed to do it, and I wasn't going to let you go unchallenged. Surprised you bothered to come back down for it, to be honest.

VENUS: As it happens, they said the same thing about you, and I wasn't going to let you chat shit about me again.

SARAH: I'm really sorry – I didn't send out the emails, and I didn't realise it was quite so-

SABINA: Well, if you'd asked me first-

VENUS: As I was saying – the piece was about how we're stronger together. I came on in a rainbow flag with *United* by Throbbing Gristle as a backdrop, singing 'Love is the law' along with Genesis P. Orridge.

SABINA: Vacuous.

VENUS: I talked about how I'd always had Asian friends, ever since I was a kid …

MILITANCIJA: That old chestnut.

VENUS: … even though I grew up in a really white town. I spoke about how the school bullies beat up anyone who called them out for picking on anyone who wasn't white.

SABINA: No mention of what it means to be in a really white town *now,* of course.

VENUS: Black, white, queer, trans – they wanted to kick the shit out of all of us. When they grew up, they used the ballot box, rather than bovver boots. Most of them. Their violence united us – or, at least, it should have done.

MILITANCIJA: 'There's more than unites us than divides us!'

SABINA: Specious liberal bullshit.

VENUS: The BNP would wipe us out unless we all stood together, I said. I played that bit from the BBC's *Question Time* where Nick Griffin talked about a non-violent 'Ku Klux Klan'.

MILITANCIJA: Easy to call out racism when it's blindingly obvious.

SABINA: And happens somewhere else.

VENUS: I didn't want it to be too one-sided, so I asked: have we become *too* politically correct?

MILITANCIJA: Thank God someone finally asked *that* question.

SABINA: "You're not allowed to talk about immigration now, are you?"

VENUS: That's nothing like what I said. Stop putting words in my mouth.

SABINA: I'm just trying to help you keep your foot out of it.

VENUS: Right, fuck this, I'm off.

SABINA: Demanding unity and then flouncing. Just like when you moved to London.

VENUS: The London scene was far more interesting. Why would anyone stay here?

SABINA: Not everyone has a banker boyfriend who can just rent them a flat.

VENUS: Not everyone has a boyfriend, eh? I'm amazed that

anyone thinks this is even worth recording, to be honest. Small town people with small town minds in a small-time scene. Good bye and good riddance.

MILITANCIJA: Shall we carry on?

SABINA: We did last time. For my show at the Marly, at least.

MILITANCIJA: The people who *needed* to see Sabina's show didn't turn up.

SABINA: And Venus moved away not long after.

MILITANCIJA: Venus's friends started some new queer disco – no performances, just parties. I can't remember what they were called – someone told me that they ripped off my playlists, but that was the closest I ever got to it.

SABINA: I never wanted to go. They probably barred me, anyway. I thought about moving to London as well, however much it would cost – the city would be big enough for me to find my people – but every time I saw a night being plugged on Facebook, Venus was all over the comments, even if they weren't actually performing. They really did make Brighton feel like a million miles from London, for me at least.

MILITANCIJA: At least you got to have your say.

SABINA: Yeah, but who's going to listen?

TIPPING POINT

....

Ed's Space

ABOUT ME
Edward
Trans man in Belfast. Writes about the NHS
& the press. Dreamer/drop-out. He/him.

- -
TUESDAY, 20 MAY 2014

Just Another Story?

I don't know why I keep going with this (apart from because of you guys telling me to). Plenty of people have documented their transitions in a better way than me – they've certainly found a bigger platform, national newspapers, *Newsnight* and Channel 4 – and besides, all we ever hear about is people 'telling their stories', which are always about their 'personal journeys' and never about housing, unemployment or healthcare, except maybe in passing if it relates to them (and their relative privilege).

As you probably know, I've spent three years on the NHS pathway – drawn out by secretaries sending letters to the wrong address so I missed appointments (and nearly had to start from scratch); getting told by the doctors that I had to 'take the Real Life Experience more seriously' after I went to my cousin Gerry's wedding as a woman to keep Dad onside, before they blamed me for 'rushing things' when he stopped talking to me anyway; by having to stop smoking and lose weight. But after all that, I'm *finally* noticing the effects of testosterone.

And, as I'm sure a few of you will understand, it *does* make it all worth it. My voice is breaking (which is embarrassing sometimes, but still) and yesterday I bought my first electric shaver – although I'm growing a beard. It's exciting, and I'm looking forward to writing more about it.

However, that does mean I can't let Dad live in denial anymore. He can accept me or not, but I suspect he won't, even though we've been in touch a little more lately. (It reminds me of how he got me into Formula 1 when I was little but always thought it was weird that 'a wee girl' liked it.) It was such a battle with the wedding two years ago, let alone Mum's funeral in 2011, but frankly, he had no right to tell me how to handle *that*.

The kids around the Cliftonville probably aren't as hard as they think they are, but there's no way to the Jobcentre without walking past them. Now they recognise me, and if I do anything other than pretend not to hear them, they'll kick off. They haven't yet but they're always looking for a new target, and who's an easier target than a trans person? (That said, the other day a friend told me about Sammy Duddy, who was a paramilitary by day and a drag queen by night, at least until the head of the UDA told him to stop after that scandal at the boys' home put the shits up everyone. He called himself 'the Dolly Parton of Belfast' apparently, but I doubt they would have messed with *him*, or not for long at any rate ...)

And signing on … since I lost my job at the Sure Start centre (because of 'the cuts', they said, but it was only *me* they let go), I've constantly worried about getting kicked off the pathway, as the Clinic demands the RLE includes part-time or full-time employment, study or voluntary work. (I wrote about the joys of being a trans man facing the public in a charity shop *here*) I'm trying to find a job – any job, whether it uses my GNVQ or not – before they inevitably sanction me. But the problem, which the Jobcentre staff and everyone at Stormont, let alone Cameron, Osborne and co. are incapable of realising, *is the jobs don't exist.*

On the plus side, I've found a community through writing here, and more recently on Twitter. Suddenly, Belfast doesn't feel quite such a backwater. We don't just talk about the NHS and transitioning, but also this recent anti-trans backlash in 'left-wing' media (turns out it's not just me who hears the phrase 'gender-critical' and immediately thinks of Alan Partridge calling himself 'homo-sceptic' …) and even *stuff that has nothing to do with being trans at all.*

Imagine!

Tipping Point

Everyone on Twitter (including quite a few of you who read this blog, as well as the loser who writes it) is talking about the new issue of *Time* magazine. You know the one – with a big picture of Laverne Cox on the front, beside the words 'TRANSGENDER TIPPING POINT' and a sub-heading about 'America's next civil rights frontier'.

It's big – big enough for the London lot to look outside the capital, although as usual, it's at the USA rather than anywhere else in the UK. (I pointed this out to them and got the old, 'Why don't you move here?' I couldn't be bothered to go through all that again.)

I wondered how many of the people arguing about it – especially the self-proclaimed 'radical' journos who are apparently 'nice' even if they spend all day demanding they go unchallenged as they insist our identities aren't real and that listening to kids with gender dysphoria is 'child abuse' – had actually *read* it.

As ever, it was a response to readers asking where the trans/ non-binary people were – in this case, why Cox wasn't featured in *Time*'s online 100 Most Influential People poll even though she got one of the highest votes. To be fair, this was better than the 'We considered your complaint, but …' crap we're usually fobbed off with, let alone the entitled whining about 'trolls' (or, as some wag put it on Twitter, 'the less famous of two sides in an online argument').

The piece repeated the shibboleth of 'America's next civil rights frontier' (as if there were no other frontiers, or trans rights were new) and made Cox their first ever openly trans cover star, backing that up with a detailed interview, where she says, 'There's not just one trans story, there's not just one trans experience'. (I liked how she talked about being taught not to associate being trans with being successful – or, to be associate being trans with *not* being successful.)

The article itself? I was expecting to be annoyed by it, even as I tried to remember that it was written for a cisgender audience rather than us. It opened by wowing at 'men in deep V-necks and necklaces' and 'women with crew cuts and plaid shirts', like they were writing a follow-up to *Lola* by The Kinks. But I guess that's standard journalistic 'colour' – we're always good for that – and it was kind-spirited, which is more than you say for most of this stuff.

It was weird how it suggested that now 'same-sex' marriage is legal (in most of the US, as it is in England and Wales but not here), gay rights were definitively *won*; I was more convinced when it implied that trans rights would be even harder for Republican rednecks to swallow. It quoted a few saying just that, banging on about 'men in women's bathrooms', doing the old 'What if I pretended to be black?' routine as though any of them gave a shit about racism, and speculating that 'transsexuals' could somehow make the US military worse than it was in Afghanistan or Iraq. (No-one mentioned Chelsea Manning. Perhaps they didn't know who she was?)

It did at least trace trans visibility back to Christine Jorgensen, even if it dead-named her and a few interviewees, especially the younger ones. To be fair, they talked to some good people: Jamison Green and Susan Stryker, who described life in the closet as 'like being locked in a dark room with my eyes and ears cut off and my tongue cut out'. (They ignored the anti-trans 'feminists' entirely – for once.)

A couple of linguistic points:
1. 'transsexual' as a noun rather than an adjective
2. More seriously, implying that hormone replacement therapy and puberty blockers have the same effect, when the former leads to permanent physical changes; the latter stalls them. (This sort of misinformation could have big repercussions for our healthcare.)

All told, the article was best when it talked about how the internet has changed our lives. It mentioned an app which points out gender-neutral bathrooms around the world, and the Cox interview highlighted the uses of connecting with people online when there were no openly trans people around you – that's certainly been my experience – and how and why more varied media representations were helpful.

Which leads onto my main point. Cox is not from a privileged background, and still has to put up with transphobia, misogyny and racism even now, but her fame does give her *power*, and insulates her from the biggest dangers of cross-gender living. (She knows this, of course, and speaks well on it whenever she's asked to.)

Does visibility equal freedom?

Why is mainstream media so hung up on it?

Will better representation lead to improved healthcare, housing or employment prospects?

Might it lead to us getting legislated *against* or beaten up *more*, as reactionaries start to learn what their enemy looks like, and how best to hurt us?

Is it going to do anything about the murder rate – especially for trans women of colour in the global south? What's going to be *their* tipping point, and how will we know when it arrives?

Dance to the radio?

I never knew what to expect from writing this blog. To be honest, I only worked out why I was doing it by doing it, and then from getting feedback from other bloggers, and especially people who came from TransNational and other forums. Gradually, I figured out people wanted me to talk less about Formula 1 or *The Prisoner* and more about transitioning via the NHS, so I did. That brought in more people, different ones who often disagreed about the services I described, some thinking they were better than I said, some that I was making excuses for them, but I kept those encounters virtual. That meant the blog still felt like a community in itself, and the comments section was like a nice local pub before dickheads came along and ruined it.

So, it was weird when my Tipping Point post went viral on Twitter. (If not 'viral' then far more shares than ever before – over 100.) Tons of people read it – even if they decided to @ me on Twitter rather than comment here. I got all sorts of responses: anti-trans feminists angry that I'd slagged them off, telling me I was 'in denial' of my 'true sex' and that I was a 'self-hating misogynist'; trans activists who said I was too soft on *Time*'s use of the wrong pronouns or 'othering us' because I 'hated myself' and wanted to be 'one of them'; trans activists who felt I went too far in criticising *Time,* because I was 'jealous' and wanted to be 'one of them'. Oh, and a few people, trans and cis, who actually *liked* it. I didn't have time to argue with most of them – I went out after posting on Saturday and was just occasionally checking Twitter on my phone – and I didn't have the heart. (I sometimes think I'm too reluctant to get involved in conflicts, but I can't remember a single online argument where I regret *not* sticking my oar in. And it drives people *batshit* when they do their worst and you just ignore them.)

I still checked my emails, though, and one was from Radio Ulster, asking if I could go on their lunchtime talk show to discuss the points in my blog. A junior producer was asking if I'd join a 'debate' about the 'Transgender Tipping Point' with the host (who, almost certainly, knew very little about it), and a journalist called Janice McAuley, presumably invited for the sake of 'balance'. (You know, like when they get an academic who's worked on climate change for thirty years up against some DUP numpty who thinks it's all a scam, probably dreamt up by the ghost of Jim Connolly or something.) Anyway, for anyone who's *somehow* managed to miss her, McAuley often gets called a 'TERF' (Trans Exclusionary Radical Feminist), which she says is 'a slur' even though she calls herself a 'Radical Feminist' and has form for calling trans men 'dupes of the patriarchy' and trans women 'dickless divas', which passes for 'progressive' in the *Belfast Recorder*. (So which of those four words offends her?)

I wrote back, asking *why* they wanted to put me on with McAuley, saying I was sick of so-called 'debate' that demanded us to justify ourselves instead of talking about any of the issues that actually affect our lives. Indeed, I told them, *these very debates make our lives harder.* My email was forwarded to the senior producer, who replied, saying they'd noted our concerns about these sorts of discussions, which had taken place around 'national' (London-based) shows like *Today* and *Newsnight*, and that the host would ensure the conversation was fair, with people being allowed to air their opinions without being 'disrespectful' or 'divisive'.

What to do? I don't want to give credence to this sort of 'debate', where our very *being* is held up as something for cis people to decide if it's legit. But if I refuse, then what? McAuley writes a column about how 'women-hating trannies' are 'censoring' her, full of insults and lies, then she gets asked back to bang on about trans people are 'abusive' and we lose even more control over the narrative. I thought it over for a couple of hours, and reluctantly said Yes. I think that was the right thing to do – what's the worst that can happen? You can decide for yourselves, I suppose, if you tune in at 10 a.m. on Wednesday, but whatever happens, I'll write about it here.

Clowns and lion tamers

The trouble with joining the circus is that you're far more likely to become a clown than a lion tamer – and even if you do, people are only watching because, even if they won't admit it, they hope they might see you get eaten.

In case you didn't listen in, I went on the radio this morning with Pat Donaghy as the host, or ringmaster, and Janice McAuley and I competing for the two main roles. She refused to shake my hand, or even say hello, when we met in the green room, which I think she thought would throw me off somehow. But it just struck me as childish (especially as she's almost twice my age) and not unexpected. Pat seemed friendlier, offering coffee when I arrived and making sure his P.A. looked after me, but his warm greetings struck me as the kind of patter he needs for his job rather than being especially sincere.

If that sounds unfair, the whole conversation was weighted towards McAuley. For one thing, nearly every question went to her first, then to me for a response, when he did nothing to stop her shouting over me. The first one *did* come to me, admittedly, when Pat asked me to explain what the 'tipping point' *was* and what made it so important to the trans community. I talked about the *Time* spread, and was just getting onto the question of how much 'visibility' improves our everyday lives when Pat interrupted: 'How big a difference does this make to *people's* everyday lives?'

Then, inevitably, it became the Janice McAuley Show. She cut across me: 'It sounds like it wouldn't make *any* difference, but it actually makes things worse. Every day, women are being beaten and raped, domestic violence and childcare services are being cut-'

'Nobody said they weren't!'

'No, but you lot are constantly insisting that everyone pay attention to you and your rights to go in the Ladies' when women in Northern Ireland *still* can't get an abortion-'

'I was at the pro-choice demo last weekend-'
'I should hope so – you're a woman!'
'I'm not!'
'Have you got a vagina?'

In the moment while I deliberated walking out, she folded her arms. Then, realising this gesture meant nothing on the radio, she said 'Q.E.D.'

I tried being 'nice', like we're always told to.

'Pat,' I asked, 'can we bring the discussion back to the topic at hand?'

'There you go, silencing women!'

I just about held it together, but I couldn't stop Pat falling into her trap. Fearing he was being an arch misogynist by not orienting the whole conversation around McAuley –

even though, by her logic, *I* was a woman too – Pat asked if 'the trans movement' and 'the women's movement' could work together. And of course, she said No.

'That's not true!' I replied. 'There are decades of work on how sexism and gender stereotypes hurt all of us – on how the right to decide what we do with our bodies is the most important thing for everyone …'

'I'm afraid that's all we've got time for,' Pat butted in, 'as there's a big breaking news story in London. Edward, Janice – thank you for your time.'

I thanked him, grudgingly, and left. I looked at my phone and saw the responses to my tweet about going on the show. The first one said: 'You know the main producer is a TERF, right?'

'No,' I responded, 'but I wish I had.'

Certainly, I won't be doing it again – if they do read this blog, perhaps they'll figure out why, but now they've covered something they obviously see as Flavour of the Month, I suspect they won't bother. Perhaps we'd do better to keep out of it entirely than to do something as stupid as the circus I took part in this morning.

Somewhere, over the Rainbow ...

Lots of (okay, several) people wrote after the last blog asking if I was going to quit writing here. Don't worry, I'm not going to – although I'm still not quite sure who it's for, so when it stops being fun, or at least cathartic, I'll pack it in. It's weird to think back five years, when it seemed like every man and his dog was doing this, and seeing who went into the mainstream, who kept going and who gave up; which sites got taken down and which just stopped getting updated. None of the bloggers I knew have become part of this 'new wave' of trans activist-journalists writing for the *Guardian* or other mainstream 'left-wing' papers, or even their websites, and most of the links on this page are long dead.

Whilst I like having complete control over what I write and publish – far away from those editors who kept telling us that 'no-one is interested in trans politics' until a handful of people proved otherwise – I've never seen this as an end in itself, because it's so hard to reach those who need it. But if BBC Radio and its 'debate' isn't for me, perhaps speaking directly to other trans people may be. After the Tipping Point post, I got invited to speak at The Rainbow Project about how the media is hurting us, and what we might do about it. The last time I went, it was dominated by gay men, with only a few lesbians. (One of whom yelled 'You're a butch dyke!' when I talked about transition. The others were friendlier, but the damage was done.)

The Project don't have a lot of money (obviously) but there were nice sandwiches, a warm welcome and a few lovely people. I spoke about the McAuley debacle; the endless transphobic articles in the right-wing press that 'out' people with dead names and old photos, saying we're all deviants and criminals, just because they think they can get away with it. (Going to the PCC certainly won't do much.) I said they wanted revenge after Trans Media Watch presented to the Leveson Inquiry about how the tabloids target trans people, and trans children in particular, and that if we wanted to change this, we would have to set up our own blogs and websites, but also that we might have to get our hands dirty and write for 'the enemy'.

To be honest, I was playing devil's advocate a bit, but the audience mostly agreed. (And Sarah, the organiser, said it was the biggest crowd they'd ever had – nearly twenty!) One person came up to me at the end – a cis woman and trans ally who I'll call P., who moved back from London for a job at Queen's University in 2010, who's recently got involved with LGBT activism. She said I *had* to keep writing, as she'd never seen a trans man from Northern Ireland on the telly or in the papers, and that as I had a voice, I ought to use it. We kept talking – about our shared love of *The Prisoner*, and the weirder teachers we both had at Cliftonville Primary at different times, among other things – over the last few weeks, we've met up quite a lot.

Speaking of primary schools, I've finally landed a job as a mechanic (at a different place to the one P. and I went to). It's only three days a week, and I need more work, but it's a start, the kids are much nicer to me than the ones around the Cliftonville and frankly anything is better than the Jobcentre. In my spare time, I pitched an article to the *Belfast Herald* site, summarising the things I said in my talk as well as the stupidity of my encounter with Janice McAuley, and to my surprise, they commissioned it. (I should say here that the *Guardian* and the *Times* didn't reply to my emails, whilst the *Statesman* said they already had someone covering trans stuff for them.) If you want to read that and support a Northern Irish trans man in the papers, it's here. Hopefully it won't be the last time …

Public health

Sorry for the lack of updates recently. Off the back of a few *Herald* articles, I got invited to a 'media get-together' in London. I'd been ambivalent, for reasons familiar to regular readers, and it was only P. who persuaded me to go. ('They'll listen to you much more once they've met you. It shouldn't be like that, but it is.')

I went to the venue – this glitzy place near St. Paul's, everything made of glass, ostentatious sponsors' logos everywhere, all on the seventh floor with a 'viewing platform'. I walked around nervously, not knowing anyone. As I got some wine, an older trans woman who I'd seen in the big papers asked who I was and what I did. I mentioned my blog and she offered to help with editorial contacts, introducing me to someone from a media advisory group who told me how they were trying to get more trans journos into the mainstream. I didn't have a card, so I hastily scrawled my email on a bit of paper, and then met some of the trans 'celebs' (actors, singers, a younger journalist who seemed diffident and went on about the dangers of becoming 'the trans writer' when I asked for advice).

Mostly, though, people were interesting, and friendlier than I expected. ('The "Londoners are cold" thing is a myth,' one of them said. 'This is the only place I've ever found a community.') After the speeches, about how much progress 'we've' made in the media, against how much work there still is to do, I got talking to someone who'd worked for NHS London's Gender Identity Services.

'We're holding a conference about trans healthcare in different parts of the UK, and we don't have anyone from Northern Ireland. Can we interest you in talking about your experiences? We can pay your travel and accommodation, and a small fee for your time.'

This would be different from the glittering, self-congratulatory stuff I've always hated. It *would* actually allow me to speak truth to power – saying the kinds of things that I don't even put on here, let alone in the *Herald* with its delightful below-the-line commenters. So, there was no debate, I was going to talk. I managed to get the time off work (even if they weren't happy about me taking annual leave so soon after I'd started) and got myself over to Imperial College London. (I told them it should be more central – Liverpool, Manchester or Birmingham – but they said London was the easiest place for 'everyone' to get to …)

That aside, I was pleased with how it went. A panel of healthcare professionals introduced the day, talking about the most recent revisions to the WPATH Standards of Care, and especially the need for Clinics to adapt to meet the needs of non-binary people. In general, they agreed, the services should be more user-led, with medics adjusting to the demands of patients rather than the other way around. The explosion of trans visibility in the media had led to far more referrals just as budgets are being slashed, with a political backlash (led by conservatives and TERFs, in tabloids and broadsheets) making it harder for them to access more resources.

Then there were ten-minute speeches from trans people around the country – north and south Wales, East Anglia, the Midlands, the north-east and north-west, the Glasgow area and the rest of Scotland, London and the south-east. I spoke last, getting more nervous as each speaker did their bit. Finally, I told the room about the six years I've spent on the NHS pathway, feeling no closer to lower surgery than I did in 2008, having clinicians tell me to 'be more masculine' or 'act butch' before they'd believe that I was a man. There were murmurs of recognition in the crowd, and during the break-out session where groups shared our experiences with a facilitator and came up with some points for improvement, I heard a few similar stories.

Feeding everything back directly to the medics and their bosses was incredibly satisfying. No-one begging us to the 'think of the children'; no gaslighting; no disingenuous bollocks followed by a refusal to engage with an explanation of *why* it's disingenuous bollocks. No middlemen, no gatekeepers, no need to worry about hostile comments or casual death threats on Twitter. (I didn't dare look at the conference hashtag.) Maybe it's a plausible *alternative* to the 'debates', rather than something to run alongside, as I wrote in the *Belfast Herald*. But it seems that if I'm going to keep up this sort of dialogue, or find my way to more people who'll publish my writing, then I'm going to have to do something that I always promised myself (and, more recently, P.) I wouldn't, and spend more time in London – and maybe even move there …

New horizons ...

No new post for nearly a month, for several reasons. Firstly, I've been busy with work – we're short-staffed so I often find myself there long after I should have gone home. With all the hassle off the P6 and P7 kids near my home, I was worried about working around them, but so far, it's been fine. I don't have that much contact with the pupils and when I have, it's been fun. I even stepped in the other day to tell a group of lads not to take the piss out of a boy who wanted to play netball with the girls rather than footie with them, and to my surprise, they left him alone, at least while I was around. To be honest, I don't think any of them even *know* my background – while the hormones haven't been quite the adrenalin rush that Preciado describes in *Testo Junkie,* they have made a *huge* difference. My chin is covered in stubble, my voice has properly broken, and I've started speech therapy at the Belfast Trust. Actually, the staff at the school have been more of a problem, but it comes out in them being cold or stand-offish rather than openly hostile, so whatever – I've got friends elsewhere.

The extra shifts have meant I've not been volunteering at the Rainbow Project as much as I'd like but I still get there once a week. It's great to see some young trans people – more than I expected – coming to the drop-ins and suggesting books for our library (including the Preciado, which I hadn't known about). I wish I'd had that sort of confidence, or that sort of resource, when I was a kid. It's interesting to hear their perspective on the media, too – they're far more switched-on about all that than I was – so P. and I ran a workshop last week about the backlash against the 'tipping point' in the London press, led not by the Tories but by new recruits to the anti-trans feminist cause. (Nothing changes: it's been 'trans people aren't real because I say so' for as long as I can remember – but constantly wheeling out Germaine Greer just looks desperate. I can't remember *The Female Eunuch* and I'm pushing forty; one of the cis students at the workshop took one look at one of her columns and said, 'Who's *this?*')

There was a heated debate, too, about whether I should write for the *Belfast Herald* (where I'd covered last month's conference, as well as the media stuff). Some of the workshop attendees, who described themselves as trans allies, brought up some opinion pieces from the *Herald* on their phones, written by TERFs, DUP councillors, and contrarian bellends from failed Marxist rags, and said the paper was using me as a shield against bigotry. I accepted this, to a point, but told them I hoped that, by writing there, I'll change the minds of some readers and editors who would never read a little blog like this, and who might eventually stop putting the 'free speech' of Janice McAuley and her ilk (who still have the ear of 'left-wing' parties and influence over healthcare) over our safety.

And without wanting to look (heaven forbid!) self-important, this kind of writing has results that most people don't see. A couple of young trans guys in the sticks, emailing to say it's been helpful to see someone like them in the paper their parents read. A commissioner from NHS Belfast (the old

Primary Care Trust, now a Clinical Commissioning Group) telling me that my points about the 'Real Life Experience' are being taken on board, especially the demand that people be in employment, study or voluntary work at a time when jobs are scarce, university fees are through the roof and voluntary organisations are closing by the dozen, and that doctors' conduct will be reviewed in line with the most recent Standards of Care. Offers to write for the *Guardian, New Statesman, Huffington Post, British Medical Journal* and others.

This won them over to a point – and I think even the most sceptical could see the worth of a mainstream platform, especially when I told them that the *Herald* let me write about almost anything I like, and have hardly interfered with my copy. It was the other, bigger publications they worried about – where occasional freelancers had little influence – who also run transphobic think-pieces from a 'progressive' perspective or still print 'journalism' with dead names and 'before and after' pics.

But, I said, if I was 'selling out' to all these people, I'd ask for a lot more money. I *am* doing this to try to make a difference, I told them – and P. backed me up – and by the end, I even had a couple of pledges to support me in the comments sections, so I don't feel like I'm fighting so many fires on my own. At this point, I said, it would be easy to say Yes to everything I'm asked to do, be it arguing with idiots on the radio or the telly, writing a 'response' every time some preacher or pundit argues that letting a five-year-old boy wear a dress will bring the rapture upon us, or being expected to speak for all trans people while making sure I never claim to speak for anyone besides myself. But, of course, it wouldn't make me happy, and probably wouldn't achieve much other than perpetuating the farce I described a few weeks ago. The *Herald* feels like a happy middle-ground, at least for now, so I'll be putting the more political posts there, and this space will go back to doing what it did during the 'Golden Age' of blogging – the intimate, the rambling, the weird – whatever wouldn't fit in the pages, or even the websites, of a newspaper.

An open letter to the Belfast Recorder

This is the email I sent to the editor of the Belfast Recorder *after a piece they ran about me on their website over the weekend. If you want to contact him, the address is* bryan.oneill@belfast-recorder.com *or* letters@belfast-recorder.com. *For what little it's worth, the Press Complaints Commission site is here.*

Dear Mr. O'Neill,

I am writing in response to the hit-piece your newspaper published about me on Sunday, in the hope – if not expectation – that you will a) issue a full and proper apology and b) remove it from your website.

The piece misgendered me throughout and revealed both my dead name and clearly identifiable family details, including the implication that my father and I aren't speaking because of my transition. It also used the fact that my older brother (with whom I have long lost touch) had a conviction for assault in 1993 to suggest my entire family, including me, had links to the Ulster Defence Association, which is completely untrue. He was never involved with the UDA, but (as you would hope the editor of a Belfast paper would understand) as we grew up near the Lower Shankill, it was hard to stay far away from people who were. His conviction, though, had nothing to do with sectarianism, nor with 'the Troubles', and to dig up a twenty-year-old story just to smear a relative is the worst kind of gutter journalism.

The article also made me less secure in my job, which I'd only recently started after months of unemployment, by suggesting that having a trans caretaker would be harmful to the pupils at the primary school where I work, and that my voluntary work with the LGBT support group I help to run, as well as my journalism and activism, were somehow part of my 'sinister agenda'. It was brave enough to (mis-) name me, but not the 'staff member' who 'expressed concern' that 'these subjects ... shouldn't be introduced to children'. I *wasn't* 'out' at work – of course I write part-time for the *Belfast Herald,* but I don't imagine the Reception Class kids read that, and I wasn't surprised to see a quote from 'a parent' who said 'I shouldn't have to be explaining these things to my kids' supporting the line from one of my apparent colleagues.

The combination of info about my personal and work life made me think that your source was someone who read my blog, but the level of detail could only have come from someone who had met me – most likely via the Rainbow Project. I have my suspicions about your 'mole' – I won't endanger them by outing them, as you did to me, but I want you to know how these actions have made a group of young trans people feel less safe in our space, and might scare them away from the one place in Belfast where they could find any resources or community.

At a time when the media at home and abroad are talking of a 'Transgender Tipping Point', and people in the UK (or

London, at least) are finally getting to discuss their own experiences on their own terms, it disappoints me that your paper should resort to such old, low tactics to try to undermine someone who is just trying to get on with his own life, and help other people in similar situations to get on with theirs. Dragging my employer into your story was especially harmful, and your use of a quote from my recent BBC appearance with Janice McAuley – who disagrees with your editorial line on just about every other issue – was a nasty surprise.

I have forwarded this letter to my MLA, as well as several trans media activists and LGBT groups, and shared it on Twitter – I hope I can share your response with them soon.

Yours sincerely,

Edward McCreery.

Dear Laverne ...

My partner, P., said I should write to you. She said I should write to you about happiness, and being happy above all else. Well, maybe not happy, but content, being able to live with myself.

I look at the resolve that you have, to keep fighting in the face of ignorance and malice, to turn the stupid questions and invasions of privacy into sources of inspiration for trans people across the world, and I'm envious. In an admiring, friendly way, but envious nonetheless.

I can't keep it up. It's not just the hit-job in the *Belfast Recorder*, or their inability to apologise, or acknowledge they might have something to apologise for, even though the piece was quietly removed after my open letter to their editor went viral. (It's still cached: I'm not sure whether to keep pressing or leave it in the hope that people forget, but I won't bore you with that.)

I expected that, like you must expect shit from CNN or NBC, let alone Fox News. P. was brilliant, hiding my phone when I couldn't stop myself from looking at the article again, telling me how the people who know and love me would be supportive. My friends at the local LGBT group were also great, putting a statement of support on Twitter and giving advice on how to talk to my boss. My employers, FWIW, were about as good as I expected – they said they backed me, but the 'source' used for the *Recorder* article was 'entitled to his or her opinion' provided they didn't discriminate against me at work. It would be counter-productive to drag things out by searching for whoever it was, they said, and I agreed, although I think for different reasons. A few kids have been a bit off with me – probably something their parents said – but I guess it'll pass.

It won't be so easy to tell the bigger lads not to bully the smaller ones for wanting to play with the girls, sadly, but the press has decided that little kids who don't feel comfortable with their assigned gender are the biggest threat to world peace right now, and who am I to stop them?

I tried, I really did. After the *Recorder* published all they could find about my past and tried to hound me out of my job, I wrote a response in the *Belfast Herald,* building on points in my blog about the specific efforts to hurt me, and how such tactics have been used against us for the last sixty years or more, even since Christine Jorgensen was splashed across the world's papers with before-and-after photos and 'sensational' revelations about her life.

I was grateful for the platform – I'm always grateful for any platform. Maybe that feeling never goes away, because we're taught to associate being trans with not being successful. Some of the comments were quite encouraging – especially the one from my dad, who posted under his real name with four little words that meant so much to me: *This really isn't fair.* Perhaps he'll get back in touch – perhaps not.

But he won't be doing it through the *Herald* comments section, as I've quit my (badly, slowly paid) slot. After my last post for them went viral, they commissioned two responses. One was the usual nonsense from a woman in the DUP. Again, I could cope with that. The other was from Janice McAuley, who probably hasn't made it across the Atlantic, but her ideas are all drawn from American transphobic feminists from the 1970s, and you'll have heard them all before, so there's no need to explain them to you.

The two pieces were almost identical when they talked about how children are too young to know their gender (if they're not cis, anyway) but McAuley used her national paper column to talk about how the 'trans thought-police' are 'silencing' her. (If you put 'Janice McAuley' into the *Herald* website's search box, it comes back with 'about 700 results'.) She said the same thing on a BBC Radio phone-in the next day, and it's tiresome to know that whatever happens, people like that will find the energy to keep up the 'debate' (and the pretence that 'I say you shouldn't exist' is a useful starting-point).

But, as you know, these people wouldn't dominate 'the debate' unless someone let them. I wanted to reply to McAuley, but my editor said that 'everyone has had their say' and that they and 'our readers' felt it 'time to move on' – before publishing another McAuley piece the next week. It was on abortion rights; I agreed with pretty much all of it, but there was another piece the week after, about how the Assembly should never pass anything like the

Equality Act (2010) here, neglecting to mention the specific provision it allows against trans woman having access to rape crisis centres, and some more tweets about how you were 'a misogynist' for appearing on the front of *Time* in a red dress and heels. She'll generate far more advertising revenue for them, I guess; hate makes clicks, and that's all that matters.

I think I've found my tipping point – it's just a shame that it feels like I'm falling backwards rather than forwards. Although, as P. told me this morning, it's not that I've given up, just that I've found the places where I can be most productive.

I'm going to keep doing healthcare activism – at conferences, where I know my audience will be people who are there to listen and learn, in a position to do something constructive.

I'm also going to keep volunteering. I might not want to keep up the media fight, but I'll encourage younger people who do. Over time, anyone who puts their head over the parapet won't feel so alone, or burn out so quickly. Of course, I'll support anyone who *doesn't* want to, but just wants to *live*, quietly and gently. The two things are linked, as I know you know. I can make this decision because I know people like you *will* keep fighting, even when it seems like millions are against you, and that you'll inspire so many others to struggle, whether it's by writing one blog post, standing up and speaking out on social media, making films and TV shows, publishing books or whatever else works for them. I hope the knowledge that your work fills me, and so many others, with so much hope makes it all worthwhile.

Yours in love, respect and admiration,

Edward McCreery.

PS: For my other readers (as this is for Laverne, but you as well), I'm not going to stop writing. In fact, I'm going to try to go back to the golden age of blogging, before it became a stepping-stone into the mainstream media, or an outlet for embittered, would-be columnists. It'll just be a hobby, and it'll just be about my favourite subject – Formula 1. Perhaps that's a good form of activism in any case, showing the world that we're capable of talking about things other than our identities – if only people would let us. But if you want to talk to me about trans stuff, there's always Twitter, but better still, there's always the Rainbow Project. I hope we can meet again there …

ABOUT THE AUTHOR

Juliet Jacques is a writer and filmmaker based in London. She is the author of *Rayner Heppenstall: A Critical Study* (Dalkey Archive, 2007) and *Trans: A Memoir* (Verso, 2015). Her landmark column on gender reassignment appeared in the *Guardian*, entitled 'A Transgender Journey' (2010-12) and she has written for *London Review of Books*, *Granta*, *Sight & Sound*, *Frieze*, *Art Review*, *New York Times*, and many more.

Juliet was included on the *Independent on Sunday* Pink List of influential LGBT people in 2012, 2013, 2014 and 2015.

Influx Press is an independent publisher based in London, committed to publishing innovative and challenging literature from across the UK and beyond.

Lifetime supporters: Bob West and Barbara Richards

www.influxpress.com
@Influxpress